CW00342860

BREATHING IN LIGHT AND LOVE

YOUR CALL TO BREATH AND BODY MASTERY

Jim Morningstar, Ph.D.

NAMASTE

I salute and honor the eternal spirit in each of you who reads and participates with me in the cocreation of our world.

ACKNOWLEDGEMENTS

I am grateful to the many guides, teachers, family members and friends who have inspired and supported the completion of this work. Their encouragement has been invaluable. I acknowledge that I am a conduit for the Spirit of Breath who has breathed life into this book.

Cover design by Thomas C. Uebelherr

No part of this book may be reproduced or transmitted in any form, by any means (electronic, photocopying, recording, or otherwise) without the prior written permission of the author.

Copyright by Transformations Incorporated, 1994
All rights reserved by Jim Morningstar, Ph.D.

ISBN 0–9604856–2–7

TABLE OF CONTENTS

Jim, about six months old

ABOUT THE AUTHOR

Jim Morningstar is a doctor of clinical psychology and a diplomat of the American Board of Professional Psychologists. He directed a community mental health clinic for five years, conducted research on levels of consciousness, taught and advised in a large medical college and a graduate psychology department. He lived in Paris and traveled in the African desert countries. Other for mative experiences have been his extensive work with various personal growth approaches including bioenergetics, Gestalt, Tai Chi, yoga, meditation, primal therapy, past lives regression, enlightenment intensives, and rebirthing in addition to delivering one of his two children at home. Jim presently directs The School of Spiritual Psychology, Creative Consulting and Counseling Services, and Transformations Incorporated in Milwaukee, WI., through which he leads seminars and training programs.

In his first book, *SPIRITUAL PSYCHOLOGY: A New Age Course for Body, Mind and Spirit (1980)*, Jim shows how the pleasure principle and enlightenment merge and how we can effectively and pleasurably use our bodies en route to mental and spiritual mastery.

FAMILY AWAKENING IN BODY, MIND AND SPIRIT (1984), takes a new look at today's family – how we use it to shape our physical development, mental attitudes, and spiritual destiny. The awakening comes as we begin to see our family with new eyes and transform our old relationships into sources of exciting aliveness.

PREFACE

BREATHING LIFE INTO MUD

Without our divine spirit we are simply a collection of molecules made up of a rather small sample of elements on our planet. The Bible suggest that human life was initiated by God's breathing life into mud. I see this as a symbol of the creative act that puts our spirit into our cells and makes them a living body. Our breath is both a symbol and a vehicle to life mastery.

Certain traditions say that we enter physical existence on an inhale and leave on an exhale. It is our ability to keep breathing that maintains our life in a body. Knowing how to support our life forces in the face of dis–ease and illusions of loss keeps us healthy on all levels. I believe we have an innate propensity for health. Disease generally must be learned and practiced to a high degree before we discard our bodies. I further believe that it takes practice to maintain our natural desire to live when we are presented with the many popular and diverse ways to suppress our aliveness.

Breath mastery must be practiced on the physical, mental and spiritual levels to be complete. On the level of the body, freeing my breathing mechanism is the ultimate medicine. Blocks and stagnation in my energy flow anywhere in my body lead to imbalance, discomfort and illness. I have never heard of any disease about which I have not also heard of a reversal. The process always involves a letting go and a release of internal holding. This is always accompanied by a change in breathing. I am not suggesting that simply by altering your physical breathing you can cure anything. I believe that breathing is more than just a physical process. I have observed that the ability to alter the physical breathing mechanism under a variety of conditions, however, is a tremendous asset in healing on all levels.

On the mental level, breath mastery is the ability to clear apparent conflict and to reach harmony. The talent for hearing the Spirit of Guidance through surrounding noise or seeing the Light through the shadows can and must be developed if I am to make any sense out of my life. My life's meaning will not come from a book, a teacher or a lightening bolt. Clarity will not be developed when I am asleep. I must breathe life into my mass of mental confusion. My thoughts will not sort themselves out nor will they discover the truth by ruminating over past illusion. I must practice thinking, speaking and breathing my highest truth day by day. I can use my mind to create new worlds or trap myself in old patterns. I can change my mind.

On the spiritual level, breath mastery means living as the author of my existence, being in the driver's seat of my eternal vehicle. I must recognize and affirm the certitude of my essential spirit or I will lose myself in the maze of wonders that I have created around me. I must admit that I am one with the Source or I will live an endless search for the one who is responsible for me. Being the one who is responsible for my life is a great relief, the commencement of living a creative life rather than a reactive one. I become one with the God who is breathing life into my cells. When Christ realized and admitted: "I am one with the Father (Source)," he demonstrated his mastery over life and could no longer be hurt by illusions of loss or death. At this point of enlightenment there is no longer a trinity of body, mind and spirit, but a single unity, a divine me.

Breath is the rainbow bridge that unites body, mind and spirit. Seen physically, it is full and easy movement of air in the body. Seen mentally, it is loving intuition bringing harmony to chaos. Seen spiritually, it is the creative act that makes everything out of nothing. Taken too literally, breath mastery is endless practice of mechanical exercises, trying to huff and puff my way to heaven. Taken too ethereally, breath mastery is fervent cloud gathering that has little effect other than to keep me avoiding life through fantasy. Balanced breath mastery means taking responsibility on all levels, caring for my body, clearing my thoughts and living the divinity of my spirit.

Know it or not, we are all breath masters or we would not be here. The irony is that as we forget or deny our mastery, we lose awareness of our natural abilities. Until we return again as little children, we will not find our true home. Through rebirthing the child within me, I begin the process of reawakening. I am the only one who can reverse the process that lulls me off to sleep with the canned music of unconsciousness. Once I make the decision to wake up, I can find plenty of help. Guides, teachers, companions are all around but I must ask for and accept assistance. I believe we are all here to WAKE–UP and take the full breath of life.

Rebirthing is one of the most powerful tools for breath mastery of which I am aware. Rebirthing is attuning my breath to universal harmony – breathing in light and love.

INTRODUCTION

This book presents the science and art of rebirthing. Rebirthing is a direct and immediate means to breath and body mastery. As a personal growth and self healing technique, rebirthing developed in the United States in the mid 70's and is now practiced in many countries around the world. The rebirthing process involves: learning to breathe in such a way as to release physical tension in the body, clearing the mind of negative thoughts and limiting conclusions reached about past experience, and accepting the spiritual joy and light that result when illusions about ourselves are cleared away. On learning the technique, a rebirthee works in individual sessions with a rebirther who helps the rebirthee release fear and tension and integrate effortless breathing and new thinking into daily life. The rebirthing process is soon learned and practiced by the rebirthee individually and sometimes even shared with others. At this point, rebirthing is being taught in many different ways. I have learned it from my teachers, my clients and the Spirit of Breath. I have integrated the technique into my work as a psychotherapist.

I have only one occupation in my life – to embody and spread the love and light of God. While I'm engaged in this, it is OK for me to call myself a psychologist, rebirther, lover, father, to make money or not, to act happy or serious, none of this makes a great deal of difference as long as it does not distract me from my major occupation which leads to my inner joy and peace.

My commitment to myself is to use whatever tools aid me most effectively in this occupation. So far, the best tools I have found are my body, my mind, my family, my inner child, and my rebirthing. I say "my" rebirthing because I believe that everyone must discover his or her own rebirthing. Others can simply give encouragement and support in the process. If I find a better tool tomorrow, that is what I will use then. So far, I have grown with the rebirthing process since my introduction to it many years ago.

Rebirthing does not help anyone. People help themselves, and many use rebirthing as an effective tool in their self–help process. Tools are indifferent as to how you use them. You can use a shovel to till the earth and plant a fruitful garden or you can hit yourself on the head with it. The shovel does not care. Rebirthing could be used to dig up more life drama to justify misery. Such a project, however, is usually short–lived because of the simplicity and power of rebirthing. You tire of it quickly if your intention is not loving toward yourself. Most people use rebirthing because its clarity and simplicity allow them to quickly get past the mind and open the doors of the heart. Rebirthing is a tool which lends itself readily to self–loving intentions.

I have often found the most powerful tool

to be the most simple. A gentle touch or a loving glance at the right time can have more effect on me than volumes of explanations. The power of rebirthing is that the simple act of freely breathing addresses itself directly to body, mind and spirit. As I breathe freely, body, mind and spirit blend into a single experience of a simple unitary being – me. At my highest moments, I see no divisions. Rebirthing helps reinforce these moments into a more constant state.

One beauty of rebirthing is that its astounding results can be understood from many points of view, including the scientific, and they all fit together. The simplicity of rebirthing is that it needs no explanation to work, just a childlike faith in life itself. For spreading the love and light of God, for incorporating the transformation to living in your light body, rebirthing is one of the best tools I can recommend.

My intention in writing this book is to assist you in discovering your rebirthing – learning to breathe in light and love. ❦

CHAPTER ONE

BECOMING SAFE IN YOUR BODY AND YOUR WORLD

Rebirthing is the science and art of increasing the safety you feel in being alive in your body. This safety leads to a sense of inner peace, abundance, pleasure and intimacy. Only by increasing this sense of inner safety can we truly relate to others without fear and defensiveness. This is the key to changing the course of survival on our planet.

OUR BODY IS OUR VEHICLE TO SAFETY

Our body is the vehicle through which we experience our life. Our body is an essential element in how we live our life and how we share it with others. Our body is integral to fulfilling our purpose here. It is not an end in itself, but is the manifestation of how we are traveling on our journey. Many have tried to ignore, bypass, repress, deny or destroy their bodies in the course of their lifetimes. This is a mistake in as much as the body becomes a barrier rather than an aid en route.

Regi's childhood experience of a hospital emergency room procedure to save her life, powerfully recorded messages of fear, anger and sadness in her body. Her rebirthings helped her change these messages.

REGI, AGE 43
OCCUPATIONAL THERAPIST

A powerful rebirthing experience began for me during a body work session. The therapist did deep tissue work on my back. It felt relaxing and pleasurable. The deeper her hands moved into my body, the better it felt. I told her how good it felt and asked her to do more. She had an insight. "If you think you're going to keep me away from the front of your body you're just kidding yourself. Turn over!" As she worked on my upper chest, I began to release emotions in waves. The emotions came up so quickly that I did not have time to consider suppressing them. As she continued to work up the front of my throat, my body reexperienced a life saving emergency room effort to open up my airway. I was 15 months old. My body felt like it was being attacked. The feeling of terror lingered somewhere in my body long after the body work session was over. Weeks later, I came to realize that, in general, I viewed life as a potential attack.

I rebirthed a week after and released the illusion of being attacked at birth. After this rebirth, however, the feeling of terror stayed in my body. I could not "shake it." I did discover that I could support myself in the presence of this terror.

I did a second rebirth with my friend, Russell. I created a conscious intention to release the emergency room experience. My body fully manifested the terror during my second breath. I started to gasp for air. Russell instructed me to take another breath, but the breath did not come. He then suggested that I accept my inability to breathe. Russell's suggestion was perfect. I laid there not breathing for a long time. My airway suddenly cleared and I was breathing again. The terror in my body changed. I was still terrified but it was no longer associated with dying.

As I continued to breathe, my body turned to wood. Russell asked one simple question. "What does the little one need?" I heard a child crying as if her heart were broken. It was hard to believe that the wailing was coming from me. As the tears finally subsided he repeated his question. "What does the little one need?" I immediately found myself in the middle of a temper tantrum. I was slamming my fists against the floor. I was banging my head against the pillow. Russell protected my body without stopping the expression of my rage. When the rage was released he asked the question again.

"What does the little one need?" Now I knew what I really needed. It was my dad. He had taken me to the emergency room. The hospital staff had abruptly taken me out of his arms for immediate medical support. I wanted to be held and protected by my dad. I needed reassurance.

I stayed with my breath and released the last of my tears. Russell put a soft teddy bear in my arms and encouraged the adult me to support the little one in my heart. He held me. He rocked me. He sang to me and encouraged me to stay with my breath until I had fully experienced safety and pleasure.

Today when the illusion of terror entered my body I easily released it with a single breath. Each breath I take increases my feeling of safety. I am empowered.

Locked within our cells is the history of how we have grown as individuals and as a member of a lineage. Decisions we have made about diet, habitats, posture in our environment leave observable marks on our organs. Less obvious are the effects of moment by moment thought patterns about our safety and well-being. Every thought sends messages to our body through neuro-transmitters. Most of these messages are not acted out with gross motor activity, but are inhibited through a system of suppression and control mechanisms. This is vital to our ability to discriminate and choose our actions. The process is continuous throughout our lifetime even in sleep. Our cells are the receptors of all that we have not done as well as all that we have done. Most of these effects may be more than we can discern at any given time, but cumulative effects of patterns of thought become unmistakably part of our character development and the posture we take toward our life. The sum total of our inner instructions is how we present ourselves through our bodies in our world. If many of my thoughts are conflicting, they are sending conflicting instructions to my body and must be sorted out and eventuate in the action I take, even if it is to "do nothing."

As I sit in my chair on my porch I hear a radio playing across the street and I know I could be annoyed because it can distract me from my writing. I must concentrate harder to attend to my task. I must also inhibit a response to get up and go over to my neighbor and ask him to turn down his radio. I have decided that this course of action would be more distracting than just trying to block it out. This inhibitory response has caused me to slightly tighten my brow, look at my paper more intently and take measured, controlled breaths. My inner attitude has been conditioned by past encounters with others who are asked to be quiet as well as by my own feelings when I am asked to be quiet. Fortunately, the ball game to which my neighbor was listening ended and he turned off the radio. Had it continued or if he turned it up, I might so control my body as to get a headache or at least end up more tired after my task for having done my work as well as the work of screening out the radio.

Life is full of such moment by moment inner work. Even had I been sitting in the quiet of my office, I still would be bombarded by countless internal signals as hunger, thirst, fatigue that require second by second adjustments. My breathing reflects every shift I make. The more conscious I am of my thoughts, the messages they give to my body and resulting effects they have on my breath, the more easily I can select the thoughts and adjust my breathing rhythms to optimize the ease and effectiveness of my life.

BREATH AND BODY MASTERY

Rebirthing is the most current version of an age old practice which has helped ordinary men and women develop their abilities of thought and breath awareness in extraordinary ways. It is the doorway to reowning the creator spirit within us and, as such, helps us step out of our ordinary restrictions. Those who have used and stayed with the process have transformed their bodies and their lives to be more in alignment with their true spiritual nature.

What makes this process so powerful in its transformative qualities? — the Power of the Breath, accessed in a way that allows us to challenge our greatest fears and therefore our greatest limitations. The beauty of the process is that it is available to each and every one of us at all times. The danger in the process is that we do not trust ourselves to wisely use this power. We are afraid and continually hide our true potential behind personal and social restrictions. Rebirthing or some version of it has been the process which has broken through the veil of fear and ignorance for countless leaders in their fields and has helped them surpass the limits to which others have resigned themselves.

Why haven't you heard about rebirthing before? You have not only heard about it, called by other names, but you have also had mini-experiences of it from time to time and have not known what it was. Without the proper guidance and encouragement, we shrink from the natural power within us and restrict it beyond recognition, letting it resurface only in times of dire need.

"Breathe deeply and count to ten" is the advice given when helping someone control overpowering feelings.

"Breathe easy now, you're safe" is the consolation given when someone has come through a harrowing experience.

"Keep breathing and stay conscious" is the encouragement given a person who is in danger of passing out or dying.

"Steady breathing" is the goal aspired to by athletes who want to enhance concentration or endurance.

"Breath awareness" is the means by which spiritual students and teachers expand their consciousness.

"Take a breath and relax" is the universal comfort given to those who are very tense or uptight.

The list goes on about the common ways we master emotional or psychological states through changing our breath pattern. Few of us, however, have fully discovered how deeply or how high we can go through the conscious use of our breath. We have not had the teachers, the example, nor the experience of going all the way past our present barriers.

Breath is the means by which we sustain aliveness in our bodies and either increase our experience of safety and pleasure or reinforce our feeling of suffering and pain.

Rich tells of his experience of using the rebirthing process to release and renew the aliveness and innocence of his body.

RICH, AGE 46
MUSICIAN

My most significant rebirthing experience was my first with Jim Morningstar. I had come to Milwaukee, through the guidance of my search for Spiritual Light and the evolving circumstances of my life. I knew that my reason for coming to Milwaukee was to complete the healing of my body, mind and soul which had slowed down in San Francisco.

These are my recollections of my rebirthing session with Jim. I remember that part of my dilemma was my inability to feel free within my body and to feel freedom through the touch of others. As I began to relax, I remember that I began to go into a very deep and dark place. As my breath began to take control of my consciousness of physical breathing, I began to feel as if I were floating out into the cosmos and that I was regressing or returning to the womb. Once I was there, I felt the pressure of form coming in at me, as my conception of myself was purely mental or consciousness. I remember feeling a tremendous fear of coming out of the womb, knowing that I was connected to my mother and that this could be a very serious separation. Everything was in motion and as I began to emerge I felt tremendous pain throughout my entire physical body. Then, as I began to drift through my years of development, I would have flashes of my body registering pain through many traumas that were being administered through my mother physically and through relatives and other adults psychologically. The messages were loud and clear that touching was a bad thing and that sexual feelings were also a bad and somewhat evil thing. I guess that not wanting to accept this reality is what may have kept me from going absolutely crazy. Because I couldn't accept that this was the way that humans were supposed to treat each other. My body then started to become numb and I knew that I was moving into contortions and being in positions of tetany. I remember Jim reassuring me that it was okay to feel these things and to continue to breathe through them. My realization was, as Jim brought me to my awake state, that I had not really been allowing all the pain that I had experienced since birth to actually process itself through my body, and that the records of all my painful experiences were passing through my body. It was a tremendous deep pain, as if it had burned its way into my soul. I realized that I had been withholding love from everyone that I had ever met, because of my fear of pain. I also realized that I was afraid of being present in my body when I touched others and was not present when others touched me.

It was a relief that I was able to give myself permis-

sion to touch with the totality of my being and to feel all the spectrum of my feeling range that enters my body and consciousness.

I am now able to stand firmly in my awareness and love and be loved.

REDISCOVERY OF REBIRTHING

It was through pushing his boundaries that Leonard Orr in the early 1970's rediscovered the breakthrough potential of his own breathing.[1] Through his breathwork experiments in a sauna and hot tub, he resurfaced the emotions and deep-seated thinking patterns stored in his body and mind. With conscious loving support he was able to help himself and others to release their stored trauma and breathe more easily. By reprogramming and replacing negative thinking with more constructive and affirming thoughts and by retraining the body to breathe more fully a new strength and quality of aliveness began to emerge. Since the time of his courageous experiments, we have learned a tremendous amount about guiding people in their original breakthrough and helping them integrate and sustain greater energy in their lives.

1 Orr L. and Ray S. REBIRTHING IN THE NEW AGE. Millbrae, CA: Celestial Arts, 1977

Leonard Orr had rediscovered what countless humans throughout history have in times of crises which push them beyond limits of everyday living: a mother has the strength to lift an automobile off her child, a wife can sense when her husband in another city is in danger, a scientist who has stayed awake for days working on a problem finds his solution in a dream. We have untold powers within us. We can release restrictions that we considered immutable. When we do, we suddenly see ourselves and our world with new eyes, we feel a new certainty and we experience an assuredness in our body that needs no outside validation or confirmation.

HOLDING FEAR IS DANGEROUS

What inhibits the full flow of life energy through our body is our fear held in place by our negative and self-limiting beliefs. We did not invent all of our present limitations, but we are responsible for accepting and embodying them. Until we wake up to our lost potential, we accept and live out our particular brand of struggle. Our bodies experience, record and repeat this struggle and as such appear to be the problem or the "bad guy" in our drama. "If only I were more pretty, weighed less, could remember better, run faster..." - the list is endless - "then I would be happier." It is our body which takes orders from our mind, carries out the instructions and then is criticized for the results. It is our mind which judges our body, perceives it to be too this or that and not enough of the other. It is our mind which buys the prevailing beliefs about what is beautiful, competent, normal, etc. It is our mind which tunes out the feedback from inside in favor of the acceptance or approval of the outside. It is our mind which overlooks and suppresses the innate impulses to self-care and self-expression. It is our mind that has turned off the incredible potential of our spiritual essence and then sees the problem as our body. It is the mind that instructs the body in the lessons of limitation and fear and carries them out through restriction of our breath. It is our mind which can reverse these numbing and stultifying instructions and open the body through the breath to recovering its sense of vitality and aliveness. It is only we who can open our minds and begin this process of recovery.

Fortunately, we are connected and can support each other in this process of relearning our true potential. As we share our discoveries and grow in the knowledge and practice of breath and body mastery, we affirm our common mission to help our brothers and sisters. To accept this calling is to reawaken our common body, to take responsibility for the course of our evolution. How we treat and educate our bodies is directly reflected in how we treat the body of the earth upon which we live. We breathe with the earth. We cannot save the earth while we are destroying our own bodies. We cannot give what we have not integrated. This lesson is crucial. Each one of us is a cell in the universal body and responsible for our sector of the planet. Treating our body with reverence and respect, pleasure and delight, will directly translate to our environment. Our next breath sends the message of liberation to our world.

To stay within our old limits of fear and repression is to condemn ourselves and our world to a coffin of restriction. Staying within our prison of self-limitation is the most dangerous course we can take. It insures our death through predictable suffocation of body, mind and spirit. It is through the loss of breathing space that we drain the play and creativity from our life and, like the rats who are experimentally crowded together, turn on each other. We begin to blame each other and to try to extract our lost life from other bodies. We try to subjugate them and reown our power by limiting theirs. We try to get back our vitality through contact, sexual or otherwise, with their bodies. Or we take from the body of the earth in our imbalanced way. Whenever we lie about our own potential and try to get from others what we have denied ourselves, we create imbalance and help to reinforce the negativity and limitation in others. In so doing we again affirm our connectedness, but in a negative way. We pull each other down to our lowest common denominator. We reinforce fear and the illusion of mutual victimization. To rise above this negative sink is to seriously take up the spiritual path.

EMBODYING OUR SPIRITUAL PATH

To be effective, a spiritual path must be embodied, it must be put into practice. To think high thoughts while holding on to stress in the body is to perpetuate a self-lie. Our bodies must be brought on board in the spiritual journey. We must practice taking responsibility for what we put into our bodies from the food we eat to the breath we breathe, from the thoughts we take on to the feelings in which we immerse ourselves.

As we breathe we are giving instructions to our body. We are translating our spiritual intentions into mental instructions to our body. We are doing this breath by breath. Not being aware of what instructions we are giving does not stop the process, it simply makes it unconscious. Rebirthing is the process of bringing to awareness the spiritual intention and mental instructions we are incorporating. It is making the spiritual life real by demonstrating how we are using or abusing our creative spiritual energies.

Jesse uses her rebirthing to bring to light the negative seed thoughts from her early life into which she was still breathing life. Making them conscious allows her to have choice over them.

JESSE, AGE 45
TEACHER

My most meaningful Rebirthng was my last one. I went into the session with a feeling of isolation and loneliness. I talked about my feelings and traced them back to unreleased guilt around my mother's death. The feeling I had about my body and myself in general reminded me of the feelings, to a lesser degree, I had about my mother before she died. I had thrown her away in my mind. Her body seemed used up and I wanted her to stop suffering and die. I felt contempt for her body and now I felt contempt for myself. And as I had mentally thrown her away, I was throwing myself away. A sort of tit for tat - feel that way for your mother and you will feel that way for yourself.

Into this awareness, I brought my breath. After breathing for a while and following my experience into the deepest part of me, I felt as if I was being born again. My body was surrounded everywhere by my mother's body. Once again, as I have in previous rebirthings, I experienced the sensations of being held in an uncomfortable position waiting for my mother to let go so I could be born. I felt myself start to fight, to force, to resent. But this time, I noticed that this struggle seemed to make her tighten even more so I stopped and let go. When I relaxed so did my mother which allowed me to drop and slide effortlessly. In my excitement to be born, I started to move faster and to force. My mother became frightened and tense. Once again everything stopped. When I relaxed so did my mother, when she relaxed, so did I. We started to do the birth dance in cooperation with each other, taking care not to push too hard or move too fast, moving with an energy that was thrilling and ecstatic. Somehow my birth reminded me of her death. The dance of birth and death seemed the same to me.

Then I became aware of my mouth. It felt unfinished, not fully formed, yearning for my mother's breast. I remembered she hadn't breast fed me because the doctors were afraid that her earlier T.B. would somehow endanger me. I felt as though I could smell her milk but she wasn't giving it to me. I became aware of the rubber substitute in my mouth and felt frustrated and dissatisfied. I remember sucking and sucking trying to make it hit the spot. But it never did. It reminded me of that feeling of yearning that is always more or less in my awareness.

Negative seed thought: what I want is not available, I can't have what I want. What I have doesn't hit the spot.

I feel my mother's pain of not being able to breast feed me: of having to throw away her milk because something was wrong with her body and body fluids. Waves of empathy and forgiveness.

Negative seed thought: What I want and need is dangerous and might kill me.

Big ahas! Lots of understanding about my fear of desiring anything.

In the beginning the awareness may be a bit overwhelming, dizzying. We may tend to deny it because of its far-reaching implications in every aspect of our lives. Our old belief systems take on a structure and a seeming life of their own. This is part of what we refer to as our ego. Its origin is both positive and negative. It is negative in that it holds fast to some version of our limitation as beings. It is positive in that it tries to help us survive and do the best it can given these limits. Therefore it will fight to survive. The drama of life is really inside us. The "good guys and bad guys" are versions of our own belief systems fighting for ascendancy, each having an aspect of the truth but trying to take over and run the world on limited information and therefore doomed to failure. It is not until both sides get together and cooperatively find the whole truth that a genuine equilibrium can be gained.

Each of us has come to the planet with our unique version of the truth. As we resolve the differences within us, we more clearly present the messages we are here to share with others. As more and more find and express their truth in a cooperative manner, the world dialectic becomes increasingly healing. Our bodies become vehicles for the message of light and love that we are here to share. The breath becomes freer and easier within us and we breathe easier as a planet.

All must be heard. Each breath, each voice is integral to the whole picture. This does not mean that every message is equally true, but each is a true expression of one point of view. As such each is an aspect of our potential, positive or negative, and must be taken into account if the totality of who we are is to be realized. It is only by realizing my full potential for creation and destruction, that I can consciously direct life on all levels.

The daily practice of breath mastery is essential for any lasting gain in our evolution or our happiness. Insomuch as we have a body and are living on this earth, we on our highest levels have chosen to evolve through this vehicle. We can hide, scream and complain about it or pretend that we did not choose to be here, but this just does not hold true. It is a lie and like every lie will cause pain – down to our final breath if we hold onto it that long.

BREATH MASTERY AS A REQUIRED COURSE

Growing up spiritually is not about becoming somber and ascetic. In fact, I believe, it is about becoming more joyful and childlike. This does not mean irresponsible, however. The true spirit of simplicity is the most responsible. To accept the simple truth that I am a child of God and as such breathe the breath of God, transforms my life. It takes me immediately out of the victim position and puts me in the student position. I am here to learn about and grow into my divine heritage. I am here to live in the Garden and come to own it. I am here to nurture my body and let it vibrate with God–frequency. I am here to breathe aliveness into the matter of our earth.

As a friend of mine once told me, this is a required course. It is not an elective as to whether we want to learn from being here in a body. We are learning day by day at a pace that we try to regulate often with suppression and diversion. We are reaching conclusions with every breath. Sadly, many of the conclusions may be simply reinforcing old negative programs we have assumed or invented. Operating on these conclusions is producing results. If the conclusions are negative and in opposition to truth and divine principle, then our experience will be of pain and frustration. Even the pain and frustration are not bad, if we learn from them. Even in suffering the body is giving us invaluable feedback. If we ignore it long enough, however, we will create our own demise. As children of God we have the right to do this. Our free will won't be compromised or taken away. We can limit our options and deny our potential as much as we want - but it hurts. Our body's loving duty is to remind us of the course we have chosen. It is our duty to wake up to it and steer ourselves in the direction of the light.

The core of rebirthing is spiritual. It is directed first toward a breakthrough of present limitation in mind and body. Second, rebirthing supports a continual building upon this new experience of self and life - a growing into new consciousness and a manifestation of a new way of living in our body and on our planet.

It takes an act of great courage to go past present limits. It takes even more perseverance to sustain a life beyond the old limits. A daily practice of breath awareness and continued experimentation is necessary to change our bodies and our planet. The rewards are immediate. Yes, I may have a vision of world peace and harmony, but this will not be enough to sustain the work it takes to incorporate permanent changes. I must begin to experience the difference free and easy breath makes to my body and my relationships. I must accept the experience of new levels of aliveness and release the fear attached to this power. It is not enough to visualize peace, pray and hope. I must breathe aliveness into my body and learn to live it. Scary as this may be, its rewards are very pleasurable. This is not a pleasure that isolates me or takes me into addiction. This is a pleasure which connects me to those around me with a heightened sense of essential family belonging.

Cathey, who has received and given many formal rebirthing sessions, shows how she extends her conscious breathing practice into her daily life.

CATHEY, AGE 57
NURSE/REBIRTHER

My most significant rebirth is my daily commitment to using conscious connected breathing in my everyday life. Breathing consciously assists me:

in continuing to keep fit and healthy, that is, to heal my physical body, to eat balanced meals and to exercise regularly

in not allowing my emotions to control me; in mastering my negative feelings, changing my negative "thots" to those of gentle self-love in maintaining my sense of equilibrium, in staying calm, centered, and balanced, breathing quietly with attention to where the "spirit of breath" leads me.

My rebirthings in the bath tub are my most significant rebirths because I am assisted in being more conscious of the present, focused and in the here and now. I become aware of consciously choosing my "soul-spirit" to lead my outer form, which is my personality. "The spirit of breath" is my most significant rebirth on an ongoing daily basis assisting me in serving as needed, in expressing my divinity, in healing not hurting, in continuing to use creative ways of interacting in my daily situations. It assists me in listening to my inner guidance on a moment to moment basis.

My most truly significant rebirths come doing dishes, scrubbing the floor, answering the phone or taking care of my sweet grand daughter. I listen to the "spirit of breath" lead me to the experience with the divine.

I am committed to allowing the "spirit of breath"to continue to lead me.

Even though breathing practices are as old as civilization, we are just beginning to scratch the surface of what breath and body mastery can mean for us at this time in our world. Breath mastery cannot be passed on any more than enlightenment can. Each of us must follow our unique path to the truth. Yet we are here to learn, teach and inspire each other along the way. Yogic techniques of breathing have passed on to us methods of calming and centering our mind and even regulating the body's parasympathetic nervous system, thereby controlling blood pressure, heart rate, body temperature. These techniques are invaluable. Rebirthing goes beyond the scope of these types of body control. The connected rebirthing breath will take us to a place of calmness and heightened aliveness and presence in our cells by innervating also the sympathetic nervous system. It will help us clear our past associations with the "fight/flight" reactions which were traumatic and took us into patterns of holding or chronic fear. Most of these patterns are unconscious and therefore inaccessible to many verbal healing techniques. Rebirthing takes us to the core responses to life and gives us choice in them. It shows us that there is no fear that can completely destroy our faith. This is more than a mental demonstration, it is a physical/mental/spiritual awakening. Because it is so comprehensive, it is irrefutable to the soul. It revives deep memories of our natural state of being beyond limiting familial and cultural patterns. It is homecoming.

Everyone's input is valuable in this required personal and planetary breath mastery course. It is important to learn from what we already know, to have guidance as I learn this rebirthing breath. The rebirther's role is to help point the way and open the door beyond fear. This relationship between rebirther and rebirthee is a model for a new level of student/teacher relationship. A trained rebirther will learn from the rebirthee as well as teach. Gradually, the teacher in each one of us is awakened and works in concert with the student in us. This inter connectedness is represented by the one breath that is common to us all. We each are called to know this breath intimately and to let it lead us to the recovery of our bodies and our planet. You are already taking this breath.

THE GREATER GOAL - OUR PLANET

Breath mastery for the sake of inner peace and harmony, individual happiness and prosperity will only take us to a certain level of success. I must transcend the small "self" of my individual desires and needs in order to access the power of the universal good. Ultimately there is no conflict between the good of the individual and the good of all, but my individual limited perspective cannot see the needs of the whole. I must transcend or release my personal perspective to truly follow the spirit within, the spirit of breath. The full power of the universal flow will by definition be impeded and restricted if all I offer is my small self as a channel.

Surrender to the Greater Self of which I am a part will open the door to a power greater than little me. This has been called dying to the self or sacrificing to the greater good in some traditions. This is fraught with tremendous fear, fear of death to be exact. It is the death of the small ego as the dictator of choice in our life. Our choices are given over to a power that does not conform to our conventional logic or even common sense. This leap of faith requires facing our biggest fears. We cannot do this if we cut ourselves off from the main channel for life energy - our breath. If we breathe fully with faith, we are rebirthing and all spiritual help will be at our disposal. We will be breathing not only for ourselves, but for the good of all our brothers and sisters as body. We will be breathing for the body that sustains us all. We will be breathing for the Earth. Some form of intention that goes beyond our small self such as to be able to teach others, help in their healing, promote harmony in our family or community, is necessary to access the full power of the spirit of breath. It is not necessary that we be thinking of this greater good every moment. That we have this intention behind our work, however, is the key to going beyond personal limitations. This opens the door to what looks like miracles to our limited self because the results are beyond its limited comprehension. These miracles in our life become more and more commonplace, e.g. healing in ourselves and others, gifts of grace and love, as we breathe in universal consciousness.

The Breath is essentially creative energy. Breath is not only the physical act of inhaling and exhaling, it is also the movement of the Creative Spirit, the Spirit which makes and sustains all. I can and have been ignorant of the tremendous power within my breath and thereby breathe creative energy into my fears and limited intentions. As I open to my true breath I start to change the effects on my body each moment. I select intentions that have immediate effects on my body, even if I do not immediately realize this. My breath is the bridge from the realm of spirit to the domain of matter. My breath is the creative energy that transforms my body.

BODY AS PRODUCT OF MANY LEVELS OF BELIEF

Our bodies are the products of many levels of belief that have come together in our unique personal manifestation. We have already talked about the effects of our personal beliefs on the formation and maintenance of our physical form. We have also accepted many of the beliefs of our family. We can fight against these beliefs or accept them as part of our way of doing life. We are responsible for knowing them, how they help or hinder us on our path, and choosing to keep or change them. This includes belief patterns about inherited strengths and illnesses. On some level of our being these are chosen as the challenges on our route.

Our families are also in part products of our cultures. In coming into this life, our bodies are also the product of societal beliefs, e.g. proper ages for children to walk and talk, how in harmony our bodies can be with Nature, who is attractive to us or not. We have taken on many of these beliefs and operate within them as guides and checks to our physical development. Even broader and more far reaching to our bodies are the planetary beliefs that we adopt in coming here. This goes from the organ level down to the molecular level of our physical makeup - how organs function and work with each other to our carbon based system of molecular bonding. Our bodies operate within these levels of connection in great part for our convenience out of our waking consciousness. If we had to consciously redecide each morning what functions our organs would perform and how our molecules would bond together, it would surely occupy most of our waking thoughts. Our bodies are a collection of many layers and levels of such beliefs that we sign on to in being born. The deeper and more universal these beliefs are, the less we seem to have conscious control or the ability to change them. Ultimately there is a level of universal belief and the laws which govern them about our bodies. These laws are accepted by us on higher levels for the purpose of carrying out our spiritual purpose in material form. They govern the translation of energy into matter and the manifestation of material from the spiritual. We all have the inherent ability to know and direct our bodies from the deepest principles. It is beyond the purview of most of us to make all this conscious at this time. It is sufficient to have faith in our higher self and its wisdom in creating our bodies for our greatest use. The breath can take us to investigate all these realms. If it is on purpose for us, any and all of it will be revealed. It is not there for idle curiosity. As we grow in mastery what we need to know will be revealed in its proper time. Faith in and responsibility for our body as a product of divine breath given and selected by us as our individual vehicle for evolution is sufficient for taking our next step.

HARMONY IN BODY AND PLANET

Embracing and owning the call to body mastery does not mean going for some ideal of physical perfection. It means using our body consciously, directly and pleasurably en route to spiritual fulfillment. This may be through accepting and going beyond what we consider disabilities to find the spiritual powers behind the illusion of lack or dysfunction. Do not judge or criticize other bodies. You may have no idea what mastery is being achieved through that particular form.

As I accept my personal mission in my body I bring together all of the levels of belief that make up my physical manifestation - the personal, the familial, the cultural, the planetary and the universal. In so doing we demonstrate this unique harmony we create among all these levels of beliefs. We are bringing together our selection of all the personal choices we have made from the many options in our personal existence. Further, we manifest the combination of beliefs we have adapted from our family and the family options to which we have been exposed. Beyond this our body reflects the constellation of cultural beliefs that we have brought together and used in creating our lifestyle. From this perspective our body is a mini-United Nations bringing together belief systems from around the world in a single form. We have selected all our beliefs, consciously or not, from a great diversity, many of which are blatantly in conflict. How we put them together, go for the synthesis in the dialectic, is our own miracle. We must take divergent beliefs from warring factions and bring peace to them within the world of our body. We thus show to those who believed that one race or nation could not exist with another, that they can and are being incorporated into one body. An obvious example of this is a child with parents from enemy camps who embodies many of the traditions of both parents, loves them both and lives in harmony with the world he draws to him.

We do not have to do extensive genealogical research to experience the conflicting voices that vie for our attention within our own body at any one time. My body reflects the splits in my self-image all the way from the obvious "good me/bad me" to the more subtle preferences I have which vary from moment to moment. I must listen to and harmonize these divergent aspects of my self even though I may not have seen the bodies of my parents or my peers do it.

On deeper levels my body is blending combinations of planetary and universal beliefs in ways which are critical to the continuance of our world. My success in creating this harmony makes it easier for you to live here. Your success in living in your body inspires me in ways that you may never realize.

Only in trusting our highest intention can we ever hope to harmonize beliefs within our body that others have not. Our breath helps us rise above the warring factions and see the universal principle which unites and serves both sides. Our breath is the thread which runs through all levels and takes us directly to Source, faster than any scientific or analytic process ever could.

Letting the breath direct us to body mastery is one way of contributing to universal peace. It leads us to know how to talk to all people and see past their differences to this common bond. Breath is the common bond and the greater vehicle than our individual body. Breath is the connector to the Creator vehicle or universal body. Our earth is a reproduction of that greater vehicle upon which we are all riding. If any one of us on this vehicle is in trouble, we all participate in the energy this creates. If there is a leak in our universal vehicle, we all experience the effects. Its effects are apparent in the bodies of the concerned and the effects are felt by all bodies on board. We are here to heal all bodies in our world, not just our own. This does not mean we are doomed to failure because others lack of responsibility. It does mean a critical part of our mission, and therefore our success in it, is giving our highest to those on the trip with us. We cannot force them to accept what we have, but we can overcome our fears enough to share the best of what we have discovered. This may not be in a public forum, nor with great crowds, but it is most certainly with those drawn to us in our life. There are no accidents in this regard, and we must listen to hear those with whom we are called to share, with whom we are called to breathe together.

Breath is the common denominator for all bodies on our planet. Breath is the channel through which life comes and love is shared. Loving intention combined with breath is the process of recreating life in our body and maintaining the universal vehicle which supports our bodies. If there ever was a time for us to breathe together in common loving intention, it is now. It is time for us to discover our own rebirthing.

CHAPTER TWO

DISCOVERING YOUR OWN REBIRTHING

Rebirthing has been for me a doorway to new life, aliveness, peace, certitude and creative challenge. It has opened new worlds of self–discovery that have transformed my relationship to my body and thereby the quality of each moment of my life. It has begun for me a voyage of self–discovery par excellence. Just as I had to discover my own rebirthing, so do you and so does every person. To be sure, we can have guides and inspirational companions; but in the end, I am the only one who has what it takes to open that door to my full creative potential. I must face the dragons that have made me shrink back from being my true self.

I have had the gift of being present at the rebirthings of courageous and dedicated men and women nearly every week of my life for the past sixteen years. This has been a privilege and an inspiration for me. Every rebirthing has been unique. Each individual has used the opportunity to experience the truth about themselves in a new way. This was not because of what I did for them. It is because of what they were willing to do for themselves. I merely presented an opportunity to use their own breath in a powerful way and helped create a medium of safety and acceptance for them in which to do it. Their new birth came with their willingness to challenge the boundaries of their own fears, go beyond their mental limits, own their true feelings, and embrace the guidance of the spirit within themselves. Every person's way of doing this has been different and each one has taught me more about myself. Each one's way of being has been a reflection of the ultimate potential that we all hold inside us.

In challenging the boundaries of fear during her first rebirthing, Pat reunited with some of her most profound sources of meaning and aliveness in her own way.

PAT, AGE 39
TEACHER

I was scared. What was this thing called rebirthing all about anyway? I had read books about it and discussed it with friends, and now I was going to actually experience it. I wanted to run away again, but my Higher Self encouraged me to stay. My first rebirth was about to begin.

As I began to breathe, I sensed the energy flowing through my body and this created sensations I hadn't felt before. As my fears came to the surface once more, coughing began and I felt pain throughout my body. The pain was by no means excruciating and left as I continued to breathe and relax . I was reminded to view the rebirth as a journey down a river with me as the captain of my ship. I was to meet whomever I wanted and face the issues I chose. This is indeed what I did.

My breathing had become more rhythmic now and I began to see images. A sense of peace washed over me as I saw God reaching out his arms with his palms toward me. It was so clear to me that he had been waiting for so long to get back in touch with me and had so much to give me. All I had to do was open up and receive. Later, my mother was standing beside God using the same gesture and smiling. This was my first real connection with my mother since she died when I was three, thirty–six years ago. Their perfect love permeated every cell in my body. I felt whole again.

To this day, I continue to feel the connection with God, my mother, and my Higher Self. The experience of that first rebirth transformed my life. The growth that has occurred since that time has been rapid and has affected all aspects of my existence. I am now living in more of what I can call heaven on earth.

I had been working with body/mind methods of therapy for many years, several of which employed the power of the breath, for example bioenergetics and yoga. Given the opportunity at the recommendation of my Tai Chi teacher to experience rebirthing, I went for it expectantly. Rebirthing gave more focus to the power of the breath and trust in process vs. technique than anything I had previously experienced. The result was that I felt more aliveness and more self–confidence at the same time. There was no outside agency which was producing this inner change. I was being put in charge of my life in a way that was both scary and exhilarating. This change in me was immediately sensed by many of my clients in individual and group therapy. Several spontaneously took the opportunity to begin rebirthing in my presence. I intuitively recognized this process and to the best of my ability began to help and guide them as I had been helped and guided in discovering my rebirthing.

One woman, Beth, whom I had seen in group and individual sessions began to breathe very heavily and deeply during our regular Monday evening group. She lay on the floor and began to curl up. She cried readily and loudly and in the manner of a helpless child. I asked others to give her room and while close to her encouraged her to stay with her emotion, but to breathe fully as she did. Our tendency when there is an outpouring of feeling is to go into a closed, protected position and to restrict our breathing so as to regain control. This kind of control, however, restricts the very experience seeking release. Rebirthing teaches a different method of control which supports expression and helps me reach different conclusions. Beth was the feeling and emoting one in her family of origin. Her brother was schizophrenic and her parents heavily repressed. She began to believe at an early age that she was not OK because she craved emotional control but was responded to with fear and withdrawal. She tried to be quiet and good and had actually succeeded in going farther in school than any other family member. Lack of genuine emotionally responsive contact, however, was most familiar to her and these were the type of relationships that she attracted, especially with men. This built internal pressure and interfered with her productivity as well as reinforcing her low self esteem. As she rebirthed she was allowed to express her feelings, but not rescued or ignored. She was validated for her sadness and fear and yet encouraged to control her own breath and not collapse into helplessness. She gained some measure of success in rebirthing during this group. She chose to continue rebirthing as a means to expand her options from either "don't feel and be dead" or "feel and be crazy." I do not mean to intimate that this was an overnight process. Beth displayed the courage to stay with it and was able to differentiate from her family and eventually marry a man who is both intelligent and sensitive. They have been successfully married for over ten years.

Rebirthing helps bring body, mind and spirit into greater alignment by providing the energy to break through the stuckness of fear. Fear is experienced in the body on a continuum from absence of feeling, numbness to excruciating pain. Somewhere in between is every type of tension that we have the imagination to create. I hold my body tense as a protection mechanism. This is as primitive and instinctual as the "startle response" in all infants. If I hold a part of my anatomy tense for long enough, I deplete the energy resources available to it and cause the rest of my body to adjust or accommodate it. This throws my entire system out of balance. If this is perpetuated long enough it becomes a permanent dis–ease.

DISCOVERING YOUR BODY

When I rebirth I open awareness to how I have been holding myself physically. This puts the spotlight of awareness on chronic holding patterns, some of which I have been aware and some of which I have not been aware. This also gives me an opportunity to alter these patterns.

Not long after I had been to several rebirthing trainings, I had a client, Gail, who wanted to rebirth around a specific physical problem. She had been diagnosed with polyps in her uterus and was scheduled for surgery the following week. I asked her to visualize the polyps during the breathing session and to send "healing energies" to that area of her body. I do not attempt to define healing energy for people, but encourage them to interpret this for themselves. This Gail did. When she returned several weeks later and I asked her about her surgery, she looked a little embarrassed. Apparently when they went in to operate there was nothing to operate on, no polyps. This angered her surgeon who tried to blame her, but after all, she was not the one who diagnosed them.

Does this happen to everyone who rebirths about physical illness? Absolutely not. Nor do I think it would be good if it did. Our physical symptoms are there to signal a multilayered phenomenon and most often requires healing on many levels. I recently went through a surgery that took me deep into my own healing process on spiritual, emotional and psychological levels. My surgeon consciously knew nothing about this part of my process, but was a wonderful part of my healing. His sensitivity and directness as well as his care for my healing and strong positive belief and dedication to his work, all were integral to modeling my self–care. Had I been able to magically dismiss my symptoms, I would have missed the point of them being there in the first place and my responsibility for them. The gift of this responsibility is still growing within me.

Our body is the warehouse for our stored experience as well as the living vehicle which takes us along our path. If our stored experience is aversive or negative, it impedes the effectiveness and pleasure with which we can use our body. When my body experienced abuse and I did not have the tools to fully learn and grow at the time from this experience, it remained "on hold" or held in my body until such time as I am ready to deal with the intensity of my former experience in a more positive way. I will often gravitate toward or recreate circumstances periodically to help release or take me past the old conclusions I reached. Of course, I have the opportunity also to reinforce old conclusions, negative or positive. In other words I can prove that I was right about being a victim or gain new power in the situation.

DISCOVERING YOUR RELATIONSHIP PATTERNS

Over the past several years I have dealt with many women and men who feel at an impasse in their interpersonal relations and helpless in the face of desired intimacy. We find many understandable and reasonable factors for this in our discussions of their present behavior and their past history. Simply changing their thinking or experimenting with new behaviors, however, does not result in a desirable shift. In the process of rebirthing we have found layers of experience much more compelling than our rational arguments could ever be. Abuse, sexual and physical, is more common than any of us might like to admit. And because of its non–admission, because it stays hidden in the closet of our minds and bodies, it continues to exert a tremendous unseen or unconscious influence on our behavior.

Recently I worked with a highly motivated, talented, responsible woman, Lea, who was aghast at the response her body had to the advances of a married man. She was divorced from a man who secretly had many affairs and Lea knew how it felt to be the "unaware" party of a triangle – hurt and anguished. She even believed that she forgave the "other women" and her exhusband. Every ounce of her moral fiber and every component of her conscious belief system, nonetheless, was opposed to her participation in a secret affair. So why, when she discovered that this handsome suitor was married, did she have even the least temptation to accept his invitations to sexual intimacy? Or why was he even in her life in the first place, she wondered. As it turned out she did not accept his solicitations, but knew that she was resisting from an ideological standard to not engage in betrayal or secrecy, rather than what her body seemed to desire. She wanted to feel integrated in her position and was honest enough to realize she did not. Nor did she want to replay the same drama over and over with other men.

Lea already had some pieces to her puzzle in that her past rebirthing and therapy had uncovered memories of her mother's father engaging sexually with her when she was a child. This was confirmed as the secret of his sexual behavior with other members of their family came out of the closet. Lea knew there was more though. In her rebirthing she both saw and experienced in her body the outrage and intrusiveness of her own father's sexual encounters with her. An entire piece of her life which included being taken during seventh grade for a medical procedure (abortion), came flooding back to her. It now made sense to her why her mother from that time on withdrew more and more into her alcoholism and eventually drank herself to death. Releasing the rage from her body and having permission to say now what she could not then, took her healing to a much deeper level. She uncovered the secret within her rather than acting out another secret. She could see both sides of the betrayal drama now. She admitted how confusing it was to be father's special little girl and how she hungered for control in her dysfunctional family. She had intertwined the pleasure of this attention and even some of the more caring touch with the guilt, shame and secrecy of the forbidden encounter. Her body was literally frozen in the passive posture as she breathed with these memories. If she said anything as a child it would have threatened the tenuous togetherness existent within the family. If she said nothing, she carried the burden of guilt for her mother's death, shame for her sexuality and attractiveness, and belief that relationship meant betrayal. Bringing this back to her consciousness was painful yet a tremendous relief. Many of her past behaviors and feelings now made sense. She immediately began separating the healthy desire in herself from the drama to which it had been attached. Lea no longer had the fear of this man who unconsciously reminded her of an old attraction because she had rebirthed herself into a new level of awareness and responsibility.

Lea does not present an isolated or rare circumstance. I have rebirthed many incest survivors who are leading healthy and fulfilling lives either married or single. The drama of what is stored within us does not have to be this striking. It does not take clinically violent or abusive incidents for our body to shut down a major portion of its aliveness. I have rebirthed countless individuals whose bodies shut down as children while crying themselves to sleep or being scared in the dark or hearing their parents argue – all part of what we would consider normal conditions.

When I discover my own rebirthing, I rebirth more than just my body. Every holding in my body is represented by a conclusion or belief in my mind. Changing my mind is just as important as releasing my body, because if I do not change my mind I will recreate more hurt and pain to store in my body. I must be able to think and believe differently to truly be born into a new life. These mental attitudes are very basic to my way of interpreting all my experiences and are so familiar to me that I cannot be objective about them. I have identified with them.

"I Am Not Safe"

Terry concluded the world and his body were not safe. He was not wanted by his parents nor attended to with warmth. He never formed a lasting relationship and contacted me mostly at an intellectual level. Terry was intelligent and knew many things, but always had a hard time answering my question, "How are you today?" During rebirthing he begged me to continue with him, even when he felt pain – because finally he was safe enough to feel something.

"I Will Never Get Enough"

Tom saw himself and his world as lacking. He was certainly wanted by his parents, but his mother was often depleted and felt inadequate. She did not have enough milk to breast feed and put him on a bottle schedule that left him hungry. Though as an adult he ate a lot, he never felt filled. Nor did he ever feel loved enough or that he had enough time or money. In rebirthing he began to breathe more fully and ever reminded himself to do this in his everyday life. He became successfully self–employed, stopped carrying food around with him every time he drove in a car and is presently sharing rebirthing with many others.

"I Must Be In Control"

Bob was always dominated by his brother and was the low man on the family totem pole. He saw his life as a struggle for control. He was ridiculed if he could not keep up. He believed that to be vulnerable was to be a wimp. He learned to compete and win. He became a successful jet pilot and later president of a highly successful business. But his relationships were tenuous and his marriage was in trouble. In rebirthing he learned to let down and admit his feelings with greater safety. He began to surrender to support rather than taking total control. He became a real person to his children and his wife.

"My Feelings Are Bad"

Doris learned that expressing her anger or fear got disapproval, work and struggle got reward. She earned all her own money in high school, working from 5:30 in the morning at a bakery job to 9 p.m. at a pharmacy. She resented how unappreciated she was and eventually left for the Armed Services. She talked about her family with sarcasm and she had a biting sense of humor. Her body was greatly overweight and she was often depressed, yet she worked and traveled regularly on her job. In rebirthing she began to recover the "bad me" who harbored resentment and hurt. She became more direct with her anger and developed less struggle and more openheartedness in her relationships.

"I Am Not Like Other Men (Women)"

Tina was always reinforced for her assertiveness. Her father was not comfortable with her femininity. She learned that to be receptive or to be too sensitive she would be bossed around by her brothers. She became very competitive with men and had great difficulty in her medically allied profession whenever she had a male boss, which was frequently. This drive also affected her social life and though she thought she wanted to be married and have a family, she drove men away. In rebirthing she came to accept her sensitivity and support her femininity. She has been practicing this for several years. She is still a powerful, direct woman, but her laughter and softness are much more in evidence. She is presently living with a long term boyfriend whom she plans to marry.

"I Can't Have Intimacy"

Betty was the product of an interracial marriage. She was youngest in the family and "Daddy's

Little Girl." Daddy lived a double standard and was an active business man, pillar of the community, but had his affairs on the side. He taught Betty to perform well and be independent. She learned her lessons and is a top executive in an international corporation. She considered herself highly successful in her field, but a failure at intimacy. She always picked someone of inferior status and was unable to meet her match. In rebirthing she has started healing the split within her between her heart and her sensuality. She is loving and enjoying her body and her relationships more. She just got another promotion. No, she is not married or even looking for some special man at the present. She is loving her work, dating pleasurably and enjoying herself much more.

DISCOVERING YOUR FEELINGS

Rebirthing opens the heart to emotional recovery. Some of the most powerful energy we experience as humans in our bodies is emotional. It is so powerful, as a matter of fact, that we all have had much programming about it's appropriate usage. Every family's programming is different. Anger, sadness, fear and joy can be expressed with love and lead to increased intimacy and understanding or met with fear and lead to separation and loss. One of my first lessons with feelings is that if I stop breathing, I don't have them or at least they are diminished in intensity. Later in life if I go to a movie and am touched with a feeling but embarrassed to show it, I use the same technique. I hold my breath, stiffen my chest, swallow. Learning to breathe with my feelings lets me experience them full force and this may be quite unfamiliar if not downright frightening. Much of our life programming has been against this and it takes more than snap decision to reprogram on this deep level. In the safety of a rebirthing context I can express the anger that might have threatened my existence as a child.

Mary harbored a secret guilt that she had not defended herself more or exposed the uncle that had sexually abused her repeatedly as a child. As she opened her breathing and deepened her feelings she remembered a time she was being abused by him and she did rebel and inflict some pain on him in an endeavor to escape. The hurt brought such retaliation on his part that she was beat unconscious and thence forward did not resist his advances. During this and subsequent rebirthings, she was able to express her fear and rage to release her guilt. This is allowing more direct and safe relations with men today.

Not all of us have such dramatic examples of programming, but our experiences, although more subtle, may be nonetheless as profound in their effects. During rebirthing Jeff often felt sadness. Although his deadpan face suggested an inner sadness he was not in touch with its source. Staying with the sadness led to how much he missed a true connection with his father. Although his dad came to see him compete in sports, he never had the kind of heart to heart sharing for which he yearned. His mind helped him resist this feeling because, after all,

"What could he do about it?" It is precisely this type of resistance which keeps our hearts held back and our breath restricted. "Why be too open, we'll just feel bad," is the negative conclusion with which we then live.

Sadness is a river of life. If I can have the courage to breathe with it and flow with it, it can lead me to what it is I believe was lost. In Jeff's case, feeling his sadness did not change his past, but it did allow him to have compassion for that lost part of himself and open the door to bring it home. Ultimately it was Jeff who through his repression was holding out on himself in the present. This included staying in a conflicted marriage and feeling helpless in the face of it. Staying in the bank of the river of sadness and watching it go by rather than experiencing it out of fear of drowning leads to judging how bad my condition is – feeling sorry for myself. This cuts off the flow of my energy and therefore my power. Jeff got in the river and learned to cry, something he had not done for years. He became the parent for which his sad little boy yearned and he had that heart to heart talk within himself. He then took action in his marriage and began to both stand up for himself and to let in love in ways he had given up on. His relationship with his two year old son deepened, and his face melted with greater expression and his eyes brightened on an everyday basis.

DISCOVERING YOUR SPIRIT

I define spirit simply as the principle of life, that which animates the mind and body. To be in touch or at one with my spirit puts me more in the driver's seat of my life rather than in the back seat wondering who is in control. I do not necessarily know what is around the next corner, but I do feel more confident in my ability to steer my way through whatever presents itself. My principle of life, spirit, is continuous with the principle of all life, universal spirit. To experience this connectedness is to affirm the truth of who I am in my very cells. This is the spiritual awakening that is unique to each person, yet has a universal quality to it. It is the most difficult to write about because it is interpreted so differently by each person. To put it into words is to filter it through our minds and have it make sense to our belief systems. To me the essence of rebirthing is not to have a "high" experience. This certainly does not occur every time nor to every person. The goal of rebirthing is to more and more live in the daily experience of the total aliveness available to us. Each of us will extract the meaning and create the context in which we live this aliveness. Rebirthing is by no means the only way to tap into this experience. It is one of the most direct and simple ways I have found, though, to put body, mind and spirit into alignment and to notice how good this feels. I will let the stories of each person who discovered their own rebirthing speak for themselves in their words on the pages of this book.

Cathy tells us how her perseverance and will to live took her past her fears and negative beliefs to discover her own rebirthing.

CATHY, AGE 47
TEACHER

Had I lost my mind? What was I doing in this room huddled under a blanket attempting to disappear into the wall? Above all what was I doing with this man who filled me with such an intense level of fear and excitement?

I had rebirthed for almost a year and had not experienced the level of feeling and awareness that I was now. The direction was to simply breathe into my heart, to encircle my heart with my breath. The effect of that suggestion was almost instantaneous. My body took control, I attempted to move as far away from my rebirther as possible (impeded only by a wall), and hide under a blanket in darkness and breathe. I recall an "oh yeah" or "so there" sort of feeling.

My first awareness was that of being sick and tired of hanging on to my past, of hiding behind the beliefs of my parents, my beliefs. With each conscious breath emerged feelings I had never fully acknowledged before. My breath was speaking louder than any words I could utter. Anger with my father for his dominance and control, and sadness toward my mother and her final shutdown – death. In the midst of those feelings was a surprise.

Belligerence! I was aware of a real stubborn streak (a streak of which I've become quite fond). I didn't have to shutdown; I didn't have to die. My rebirther said "no your spirit doesn't have to die." So clearly I remember saying "no I don't have to die." This body did not have to die.

Yes I had lost my mind! And for what seemed like the first time, I touched my heart and my desire to live. A spark was kindled. The flame burns..

DEFINITION OF REBIRTHING

Rebirthing is the transformational healing process which involves integration of the physical act of connected/relaxed breathing, the mental attitude of resolution to the highest thought through all experience, and the spiritual intention of loving union with universal life. Rebirthing reinforces safety and pleasure as a constant state on the physical level. When I teach rebirthing I reduce the instructions to two:

- keep breathing fully, freely, and consistently;
- while doing this, continually adjust your body and mind towards what makes the process easy and pleasurable.

I liken this process to being on a river in a small boat with your hand on the rudder, steering yourself to where the current is strongest and the flow is easiest. As the rebirthing continues I lend support and safety, and I give the rebirthee instructions and suggestions for adjustments in the physical and mental process. Rebirthees soon learn to translate whatever I say into behavior which produces practical results according to their own course, and to develop the habit of automatically guiding themselves to release.

THE SIGNIFICANCE OF YOUR BIRTH

Birth is a significant moment of conditioning for the body. The moment of the first breath is also the moment the entire newborn body is introduced to life outside the womb. Breathing is associated strongly with the degree of safety, comfort, and trust one experienced through the bodily senses. If the original sensations were overwhelming or unpleasant in any way, the body's natural reaction is to contract, be on the alert, tense up. Breathing and being alive outside the protection of the womb becomes classically conditioned to the state of caution or even panic. An inhibition response to the process of breathing ensues. Research has linked such early experience to a lifelong state of generalized anxiety.

Rebirthing reconditions the early association between the fully alive, uninhibited breath and the state of safety and trust in the environment around the body. The conditioned inhibited breathing response is extinguished in the presence of love and trust that the rebirthees provide for themselves. Rebirthing on the physical level is literally a reconditioning process of the human brain stem.

I would not have believed how detailed and impressionable a memory we retain of every life experience including our own birth, had I not gone through the process myself and with many others. Doris recounts her reexperience of her birth, and many levels of awareness she had even as a newborn. In so doing she rediscovers her innate potential for conscious awareness in body, mind, and spirit. It is with this expanded awareness that we reprogram the fear and embrace greater safety.

DORIS, AGE 49
CHILD
DIAGNOSTIC SPECIALIST

My arms were pinned to my sides and I kept desperately thinking, "Let me go! Let me go!" I began to say this out loud while maintaining my rebirthing breathing. I was being born! My arms were tightly against my body as I exited through the birth canal. Then I was lying on a double bed, able to see in all directions – through the top of my head, the side of it, every place in the room and even out the windows.

I was aware of everything in my immediate environment and keenly attuned to the feelings of the people around me. My infant self acutely understood complex interactions and relationships of the adults in the nursing home where I was born, on June 5, 1938, in Eldon, Missouri.

It completely surprised me to see that I was born in a double bed with a wooden foot and headboard. There was a west window overlooking the lawn. On the south wall there was a closet.

My mother was lying on the bed and the doctor was talking to her. (In later years I knew the doctor who delivered me because he is a good friend of my parents.) In reexperiencing my birth I was surprised to see that at that moment it was my mother, not I, who was the focus of attention. I felt so vibrant and radiant with streams of energy pouring out of me. I felt impatient. I wanted to move and do and act, and I really didn't like lying there quietly, belying my tremendous energy.

Now I could easily feel the love Dr. Jim felt for my mother. I realized he was happy to be able to express it under the guise of a nurturing patient/doctor situation, and he sent the nurse/midwife out of the room just to have a few minutes alone with my mother (and me). My mother didn't love Dr. Jim. She liked him and felt happy at my birth and relief that it was over.

Dr. Jim kissed my mother. I saw it through the top of my head.

All this was later confirmed by my mother. She was surprised to learn of Dr. Jim's feelings. She said that after I was born she said to him, "Whew! That was work! Give me a kiss."

More broadly defined, rebirthing is about body mastery, what it takes to be one in body, mind and spirit. It is not primarily a belief system or a philosophy. Proponents of every system or technique for improving life have a philosophy. We can listen attentively to these theories, but we get to know a great deal of what they are really about by how they treat their bodies. Do they have particular diets, wear special clothes or ornaments, engage in rituals, interact with others in unique ways? In the name of quite similar sounding philosophies, groups have engaged in vastly different lifestyles and practices. What this communicates to themselves and their world is more than superficial. Their actions communicate their intent toward their bodies; whether they are trying to ignore and get beyond them, deny, subjugate, gain merit by struggling, glorify, or make a cult out of their bodies and its needs. The rebirthing technique, as well as its philosophy, promotes harmony and aliveness in the body through continuous full and free breathing. Regardless of my diet or lifestyle, relaxed and complete breathing can bring a vitality and focus to every activity and relationship I have.

BALANCING YOUR LIFE ENERGIES

Of course a simple breathing technique cannot change my entire relationship to body, mind and spirit. Rebirthing teaches me to breathe more freely and easily as a result of an inner transformation. This is a process of changing fixed and limiting attitudes into a lighter and more flowing relation with my world. I learn how to let go of a rigid kind of control, like that of a dam, in favor of a control that relies on inner balance and self trust, like that of a surfer. I use the power of the flow of energy, but not at the expense of accumulation of tension. I develop the art of letting go. Just as a surfer must let go of fear in order to enjoy and master the sport, so do I let go, but not by letting my life fall apart or following just one impulse. I must balance all my energies and blend them with greater artistry. This means being able to tune into my feelings and thoughts with greater accuracy and to orchestrate them more effectively. I learn to trust my natural inner healing while maintaining a grounded self–caring stance. In my body I develop the ability to take the clearest, easiest, most releasing breath. In my mind I develop the skill of selecting the most direct, inclusive, highest thought. In my spirit I reside in freedom, peace and joy.

Achieving this goal is not a matter of being imbued with some special ingredient now foreign to my system. All I need is within me. It is a matter of fine tuning my special blend of body, mind and spirit into a unique formula. This formula turns the common into the precious, the ordinary into the rare. Discovering my rebirthing is an alchemy that transforms my everyday breath into a golden light.

I have often looked at the list of ingredients on the package of a food that I particularly enjoy and marveled at how they got that taste to come out of those simple everyday elements. The elements out of which we are made are quite common, but how we blend them makes quiche or scrambled eggs. The Chinese reduce these elements of life to two: Yang and Yin. We are, in this system, a combination of the active and the receptive life principles, outgoing and incoming energies, exhale and inhale if you will. I must not only set goals and take active steps to what I want, but also be able to adapt to what comes, and go with the flow to be happy. Formulas for the good life tend to emphasize one or the other principle. This emphasis is usually because the individual or the society has gone too far the other way. If I have gotten too aggressive and am pushing myself and everyone around me, it may be time to practice yoga or take up lap quilting. If I have become unfocused or stagnant and seem to be uncomfortably floundering, it may be time to take a time management or goal setting seminar. My unique truth is in the balance of my active and receptive energies reflected as my exhale and my inhale. How I breathe accurately portrays how I be.

In the traditional Chinese symbol of Yin and Yang there is a dot of its opposite in the center of each principle. I interpret this to mean that what allows my most active, assertive energy (Yang) to produce and be effective is at the core my ability to adapt to and handle whatever comes, to surrender (Yin). Strength that cannot surrender is useless. Conversely, what gives power to my serene, meditative, peaceful self (Yin) is at its core the focused, active, discriminating intention to settle for nothing less than the divine in my life. Peace without dynamic directed interaction (Yang) is death.

Rebirthing is fine tuning the breath of life, bringing harmony to the active and receptive energies in body, mind and spirit. In my body I actively take in the air and I am receptive to the energy's nurturing and healing. In my mind I actively affirm what I want and I am receptive to the loving intention behind all my thoughts. In my spirit I actively use my creative forces to manifest heaven on earth and I rest in the perfection of my eternal self. To the mind these are a bunch of outright contradictions or at best paradoxes. The mind insists on keeping opposites separate and cannot blend the two. The blending is the work of the heart. In the heart all contradictions are resolved. The medium of love is uniting rather than dividing. It is in the medium of self–love that the true alchemy takes place and my feminine (Yin) and masculine (Yang) energies operate in harmony. My mind wonders how I can purport to feeling peace and perfection and at the same time be striving and facing one challenge after another. My heart understands that both are essential ingredients to who I am and that neither cancels the other out. They are like my two legs that work together on my journey of life. When I firmly plant my foot in self–acceptance then I can take another step in self–improvement. As I accomplish the goal I strive towards, I can rest in an even greater assurance that there was nowhere I needed to go.

In each rebirthing session I recreate that original push, that creative breath, which brought me into life. I am both the mother giving birth through active labor and the infant being born through cooperative acceptance of the process. In that original birthing I felt intense energy, the energy of creation. I also reached conclusions about that process, myself and the world around me. These conclusions are strongly imprinted in my consciousness and are the attitudes through which I view my life. I am not just the passive recipient of things done to me, I am also the active shaper of the events and reacher of the conclusions about them. This is the power of the creator and is so awesome that it is repressed and denied by most everyone. To accept this power is to admit and experience my full responsibility for my life. Most rebirthees do not do this in a single session but take a little bit at a time – just as much as they feel they can handle. In so doing they build a base of safety from which to reown their full creative potential. It is one of my greatest joys and privileges as a rebirther to witness this birthing process.

The events of my birth itself dramatize the themes which I am in this lifetime to resolve. For example, I birthed myself and came out while my mother was waiting for the doctor to arrive. In the delivery, however, my mother tore and needed stitches. In my life I have the strong theme of "doing it myself" and not waiting for help or permission from the authorities. I have also had the theme that for me to get my way (freedom) the other, especially the woman, gets hurt. I do not believe that these themes were caused by the circumstance of my birth, but that rather these themes are my own and are reflected in how I interpret and recreate these circumstances in my life. For this reason I refer to the birth events as "Birth Drama" rather than "Birth Trauma." I tend to keep my drama current until I decide to rewrite the script. At this point in my life, again for example, I am learning to work with others (including doctors) in mutual harmony for mutual benefit. I am also learning with the women in my life that getting my way can be done in harmony with getting their way for mutual reward. Rebirthing is both a cleaning of old action themes and a rewriting of my life script.

On the physical level this awakens primal energies that burn through old patterns, often felt as heat in the spine, and help me take a new posture in life – "straighten myself out," if you will. Resistance to this energy can be experienced as discomfort. Flowing with this energy can be experienced as divine bliss. As I accept and relax into whatever comes up as I rebirth, bound energy heats up and turns to light.

My breath symbolizes the movement of all life change, the ebb and flow of the seas, night and day, the seasons, the taking in and the giving out of nature, the experiencing life and growth in my body. I nurture my cells with vital elements each time I inhale. I release what is no longer needed by my body on each exhale. I continue this life affirming process whether I am awake or asleep, elated or depressed, clear or confused. This suggests that I am something more than what is dictated by any one of these states. As I tune into what it takes for me to more easily maintain my nurturing breath process throughout all life situations, I come closer to being more conscious of just how I perform this miracle of life.

I was amazed at the extent and subtlety of breath constriction involved in my daily routine once I opened my awareness to it. Some people think that they are breathing less freely after they begin the rebirthing process. They are just becoming aware of how frequently they impede their breath. Awareness is a first and necessary step to conscious change. It is very difficult not to change once I am aware of what I am doing. Resistance and fear hold me back from the discovery of the power of this great vehicle for change right under my nose (literally!). With the dawning of awareness, change and growth are not far behind.

MASTERY IN BODY AND MIND

Mastery of my breathing mechanism transforms how I nurture my body on a moment by moment basis. These signals to my physical breathing mechanism come from my mind and reflect a change in how I think about myself. To give different instructions to my body, I must operate with different programs in my mind. Rebirthing involves a process of resolving mental confusion. For some rebirthees they literally remember and see scenes from their past in which they reached negative or emotionally blocking conclusions about themselves. As they affirm the truth of their aliveness by taking a releasing breath during their experience, they send new signals of OK–ness and freedom to their bodies and reduce the old fearful holding responses. Most rebirthees do not remember every negative thought they are changing. The memory is secondary to the intention to positively affirm and clear myself. The result of feeling more clear and whole is more important than how many memories I have had. All this is the self–reconditioning process. I will tend to bring up what I am ready to release and only go as far as I feel safe. This is also crucial. I have not been pushed or prodded by anyone else. I own my ability to release myself. The rebirther is there to guide, suggest and instruct as best as he or she can, but it is I who is in the driver's seat and who is steering the vehicle. Only I know how to release in the way that is uniquely effective for me. I must discover this in the process. I would love to be able to figure it all out ahead of time and intellectually control my cure. On this level of self–discovery, however, I must trust something beyond my mind. My mind cannot master itself. Only the creator of my mind can change it.

The creator of my mind is what I call my inner breath, the movement of my creative spirit. The essence of rebirthing is the harmonious connection of my inner breath with my outer breath. The outer breath is the movement of my lungs and the rest of my mind/body. Only I know how to make this final connection and I must use every faculty at my disposal to do so. Rebirthing will call from me a greater use of all my intuitive, intellectual, emotional, mental and spiritual capacities than I had given myself credit for in the past. It will draw from me the talents and powers as well as an integration in their usage that I had not been willing to admit or display. At the conclusion of the rebirth it is my greater self that I am impressed with, not just the rebirther or the process.

Rebirthing is the rainbow bridge that takes me beyond my old self held in place by my mind. This is the bridge between the inner and outer breath, between the invisible and the visible, between the conscious and the unconscious, between feeling and judgment, between energy and matter, between heaven and hell. Rebirthing brings together what the mind has rent asunder. In the connected breath I can experience the truth that I am creating the universe as well as being formed by it each moment. Through the doorway of the heart I reach beyond my mind to that bridge of unity and reconnectedness.

I can begin through rebirthing to use my breath as the cord of connectedness. By listening to and following my breath I "hear the messages" from every organ of my body down to the very cells themselves. By fine tuning my ability to observe my sensations I begin to hear with the ears of love. This allows me to relax in areas that are tense and visualize healing in parts that are hurting. As I continue to keep my breath open while experiencing sensations, feelings, or limiting thoughts which would ordinarily prompt me to constrict my breath, I reprogram my mind and body to greater freedom and aliveness. My cord of connectedness reaches outward also to other bodies. I increase my sensitivity to those with whom I am connected psychologically, emotionally and spiritually. If I am willing to pay close enough attention, I can tune into my connectedness with all of life. I can reaffirm my unity with parts of the universe from which I have separated.

In listening to the pain in his body during rebirthing, Ray was able to release the blocks he held within his body and in his relationships with others.

RAY, AGE 41
ELECTRICIAN

Rebirthing is always a new and different experience to me. Even the times that seem the same have different messages in the days following.

One occasion I'll remember a long time. I was in a session with Jim, breathing along. I noticed a tightness in my spine just above the pelvis, a baseball bat grip around the column, a feeling of immobility. I related this feeling to my rebirther and he made the suggestion to breathe into that area and envision each breath moving the blockage up and out of my body. With focus I was able to move the sensation up my spine.

It moved slowly but freely up into a point just above my shoulder blades and entered the base of my neck where it lodged itself and began to grow. With interest as if I were outside my body looking in, I was amazed at how I worked this problem to this point. I wanted very much to continue, but I only developed a "pain in the neck."

I reported this to Jim and he calmly said "Release the names of everyone who gives you a pain in the neck."

Instantly I got this vision of a whole bleacher section full of faces. I broke into laughter. Sure, there they were, mom, dad, my sister, Kathi and the boys, my boss, friends, darn near everyone I knew, all sitting there waiting for me to call them out.

As I gained control from the laughter, I called them out, noticing there were feelings for some names more than others. I didn't want to admit to being pained, partly for fear of the truth and partly for shame that I had visioned them that way.

As I eliminated each face, the pain diminished and a feeling of calm came over me. A tingling sensation started at my feet and with each breath, slowly moved up my body and out my head.

Jim suggests I bathe in the energy and take it with me for the rest of the day. And as I write this I notice it is still with me and continues to bathe me in clear energy whether I'm aware of it or not.

The mastery of my breath keeps going to deeper and more subtle levels. It is only I who, reaching my mind's limit, can say that there is no more to be learned or that it is becoming boring. Whatever I think is the essence of breathing is simply my mind's limited interpretation. If I am willing to tune in, let go and be surprised, the secrets of the ages are a breath away. Expertise in rebirthing does not come from accumulated knowledge, it is rather a talent in releasing what I thought I knew and discovering new wonders.

This is the "game of masters" – to learn how to be present in every breath I take, to be aware of each thought as it passes through my awareness (Buddha's definition of enlightenment), to be the author, the creator, the divine parent of my fully alive body, clear mind and creative spirit. This is the challenge that faces each one of us on this planet. I am here to integrate a sense of eternal sameness and constancy with continual newness, freshness and everlasting aliveness. I am both the old, wise, nurturing parent and the newborn filled with awe and wonder. The moment of birth sets the tone for how I parent myself, how I deliver myself, what possibilities I set before me, what limits I choose, and who I see as responsible for my world. Each rebirth allows me to review these decisions and to choose with new purpose and clarity. To take up this challenge is to be counted among those who take seriously their purpose for living and who are willing to rise to their full mastery. You must discover your own rebirthing.

DISCOVERING YOUR OWN REBIRTHING

I am responsible for increasing my consciousness and discovering my full potential, actualizing the vast untapped Source within which I am me. I cannot claim that I know all of what lies beyond the boundaries of my present consciousness. The borders of my present awareness are guarded by my fears. If I am willing to accept that there may be more to me than I now know, I am willing to challenge the fear of my own unknown. I can take my next step in mastery. I must on some level trust that I am one with that Higher Power because I certainly do not know all the answers in my current intelligence. Regardless of where I stand on an I.Q. test, however, I am imbued with the inalienable capacity to think my next thought – this is my divine birthright – no matter how stupid or smart I think I am. This kernel of truth is the basis for all self–knowledge. I have the power to think my next thought and shape my reality with it, color my feelings through it and justify my behavior with it. If this thought is not in alignment with universal truth, I will be out of alignment with my true essence and with others. This will produce confusion and pain. I put my thoughts into physical form as I breathe. I participate in the universal creative act by breathing my intention into my body and my world.

I hereby am given a tool with which to examine how I breathe life into my body and my world. This is the knowledge of mastery. You must take the lead in challenging your fears and in discovering the creative power within you. You must discover your own rebirthing.

This is not a mastery reserved for some special elite beings. This is the mastery that we common everyday garden–variety divine beings are called to embrace. Every one of us who can form a thought are called to be responsible for that thought. All of our society hinges upon belief in this ultimate responsibility. No one can get away with "I decided to think murder is OK." Yet we stop ourselves short with fear, however, when we are asked to go further in mastering our mind and body. Every one of us is afraid, and everyone of us is called to go beyond our fears to the-light of greater freedom, truth and joy in our lives. This is everyday mastery.

True enlightenment does not set beings apart. It makes them aware of the essential divinity within all life, giving reverence to all. You and I are very different in our external qualities, we are one in our spiritual essence. You are responsible for your life, I am for mine. We breathe the same breath of life yet we shape it differently. Rebirthing is simply using the breath of life to discover the fears and limits which are holding us at our present level of awareness. This takes a great deal of childlike simplicity to look at our lives with new eyes and to play with new ways of being. Through rebirthing you can find one of your greatest allies in this process of change – your own inner child.

CHAPTER THREE

REBIRTHING YOUR INNER CHILD

No one has told me more about the history of my body's evolution in this life than the child within me. This child has become a principle ally on my path to breath and body mastery.

A strange and compelling phenomenon began to happen for me not long after I started rebirthing others. My rebirthing clients began to report more and more early childhood memories in the course of their breathing sessions. I, in turn, was directed to explore their relationship with their inner imagery of their memories. This started out as simply asking the rebirthee to fill in as many details as possible about their memories, including sights, sounds and most importantly feelings. At first the focus was on the child. Then the focus began to include the relationship between the child and the rebirthee. A wide variety of reactions ensued. Some rebirthees wanted nothing to do with this child. One described a brief glance at this child as "dirty and pitiful, hidden away in a closet" and that is where she wanted to leave her. She refused to explore any further. As sessions progressed, we found out more and more of the tremendous emotional charge that her little girl carried and how painful it was for the rebirthee to remember how she felt.

Other rebirthees became immediately identified with this child and lost objectivity, merging with the child's most intimate thoughts and feelings, seeing and feeling everything through this child in an altered state. This often produced a cathartic type of release, but did not always increase safety or confidence in the rebirthee as they sometimes concluded that they could be "taken over" by their very vivid memories – living recreations of early experiences – in the midst of which they felt helpless. This varied in degree. Some rebirthees completely lost awareness of their current surroundings and talked and moved as if they were living out their past experiences. Others experienced some of their childhood feelings, but were well aware of their observer role and the rebirthing setting. The most astounding awareness for me was how completely this inner child was fully experienced, as though being in their infant body taking in all the sensory input and the complete impact of them on their little bodies. My work during this time was to stay as completely with the rebirthee as possible and to help them maintain their breathing, to remind them of their safety and eventually to help them reconnect with their adult selves, to provide protection and help reach new conclusions about their present power and abilities. It became evident that such deep–seated childhood experiences were still dramatically influencing this rebirthee's self image and assessment of their present choices in life. A common memory is wanting the attention or interaction with a parent, while seeing their parent preoccupied – daddy is reading the newspaper and tells me to be quiet. The child mind seldom has the objectivity to separate father's anxieties and need for escape from an ultimate statement about his or her own worth. As a child I conclude that I am worth less than the newspaper. I may then resort to more and more elaborate forms of attention seeking or give up and isolate in fantasy or loneliness.

The importance of such a living memory is not that this one incident caused a life of loneliness, but that it poignantly symbolized the quality of relationship I had with my father. This opens the door to some very powerful reprogramming work and should be handled with great care. The rebirthee is extremely vulnerable at this point and is able to reinforce old negative conclusions and feelings. Contrariwise this is a time to access new resources, reach new conclusions and change behavior in present life. As the rebirther, I am one of the new resources present at this vulnerable time. I believe it is not my role to impose my values and/or feelings on this child, but to listen very carefully to what it is this child was not able to express or do in their child mental, emotional and physical state. Next I attempt to access the resources of the most important figure, the rebirthee. If we are able to link adult resources with walled off or, traumatic childhood feelings, then we can make a profound change in the rebirthee's inner dynamics.

I have with some success helped this healing with the inner child through visualization or guided imaging alone. Adding the full open breathing of rebirthing, however, accelerates this process by preparing the body and mind for a full sensory openness and building upon the self–regulating skills the rebirther has already learned. The rebirthee can access the cellular aliveness of the child and keep adding adult resources to create safety and direction.

Dawn is able to do this in the following example with the help of her rebirther, David.

DAWN, AGE 55
CHILD CARE WORKER

After breathing for what usually seems interminably long, memories begin to stir, images surface.

I'm at the orphanage. It's a Sunday and my father has come to visit. He looks very nice, dressed in his gray suit. He is angry at me. There are no words between us. He has once again received news of my non–compliant, rebellious and defiant behavior. I feel so terribly rejected by him. I remember the words "one rotten apple spoils the barrel." They said it to me repeatedly. I want him to love me. I want him to accept me. I feel his disapproval, disappointment, contempt. He says nothing – the very worst punishment for me.

I retreat, run back to the cottage. [David reminds me to keep breathing.] I enter. I see Sister P. I want to confront her. My feelings are mixed with rage, impotence, fear, rebellion. I am so terribly stuck. I am standing speechless. I feel paralyzed. [David is breathing with me. I feel his support. I feel his eagerness for me to "break through," to regain my power. He says "make faces at her.] I'm stuck. My body feels like lead. I feel vanquished. Slowly I begin to walk backwards – retreating to the door – my body begins to shrink. I become smaller and smaller. I am tiny now. I slide right out under the door. I am outside in the long corridor now. I regain my stature.

It is time to mop the halls. I'm dressed in the blue–gray "prison garb" (orphanage) dress. I feel plain and homely. [My breathing has become less labored. Connected breathing has now resumed.] I kind of glide down the long hallway and I enter the church. I sit in the pew. I begin to feel at peace. I am going down – down – deep – deep. Oh such peace, tranquility, bliss. My God–self is surfacing. I feel incredible love, oneness. I feel beautiful! A joining with the universe. I have recovered my power.

I forgive you daddy. I forgive you Sister P. I forgive you Dawn.

This is a strange place for me – such wondrous peace. My thoughts are quiet. I don't want to leave this sanctuary.

David is there asking "How are you doing?" His loving support is an essential part of my healing.

The early separation or split between a child and parent is always reflected in how we talk to and treat our own inner child. Even though we consciously swear that we would never threat a child like we were treated, how we respond emotionally to the voice of our own needs and wants always bears similarities to how we were treated by our own parents. They provided a constantly reinforcing model to us day after day, year after year. This concept is so foreign to our rational mind, that the most frequent response is categorical rejection and denial. To be sure, there is not a one to one correspondence in how we talk to and treat ourselves as our parents did to us. In fact most of us pride ourselves on having made significant advances in our self–care. But the more subtle and insidious expectations we impose on ourselves are so common or "familiar" that we do not recognize or admit them consciously.

Occasionally our early negative self talk will pop out when under stress, e.g., hitting our finger with a hammer, burning the dinner, feeling rejected or ignored by another. A little voice in our heads can be heard to say: "What a dummy," "Nice going (sarcastically)," "No one cares about me," or we may project blame on the world: "What jerks!", "People are thoughtless." This however always reflects back to me as someone burdened by living in such an incompetent or uncaring world. More subtle means of handling stress may be intellectualization, "I understand that things like this often happen," or placation, "It's really OK, I know they really are too busy to pay attention to me." In all of these cases though, resolution of the frustration in the child's view is incomplete. The child is left to a world in which his or her needs are not really met by the outside. More than anything, this child needs to know that he or she will not be abandoned to face all this frustration alone. My inner child needs me. Your inner child needs you. I tend to abandon my inner child in the same way that became familiar. Examples of this are as plentiful as there are families on the face of the earth. I will attempt to give some broad categories into which these negative self talk themes can be summarized. See which themes are most familiar to you.

BASIC SAFETY THEMES

Upon first entry into the world, our body is greeted by a sense of attack or a feeling of care for its basic integrity. We immediately react to these stimuli and in turn others around us react to our reactions. This gives us the messages of welcome and safety in our world or hostility and fear. Now we all have some combination of these messages. It is not a black and white issue. We can affect this balance and increase genuine safety which in turn leads to pleasure. It is necessary to go beneath our surface chatter or polite amenities to truly hear how safe our little girl or little boy feels in her or his world. Also there is a difference between a temporary or situational scare and more enduring repetitive themes. Being scared at a Halloween costume seen for the first time is different and appropriate as compared to a nightly fear of a monster under my bed.

More obvious lack of safety is reflected in chronic fear of the world, social situations, down to animate or inanimate objects. Our inner child is frozen in deep seated fears. More subtle lack of safety gets reflected in avoidances that are intellectually justified social prejudices, general anxieties or strong preferences that rigidly limit one's experience and restrict the full enjoyment of all the possibilities at one's disposal. Our inner child has some safety but has to rely on compensating defenses to survive. Thus my adult may gain expertise in certain areas, proficiency in technical or even social skills, but my underlying foundation of security is always under threat or shaky. This tends to keep me never fully or wholeheartedly committed to anything or anyone. I am always partially here and partially elsewhere for safety's sake. I think this will keep me from being trapped. I sense I never fully belong to my family and may even have fantasies that I was adopted. I am particularly sensitive to angry or hostile energy and do all in my power to escape it because I do not feel safe enough to survive. My inner child repeatedly gives me fear messages. My adult never fully listens or responds to the real issues but constructs a lifetime around partial or "band aid" solutions to my fears. The result is that I never experience complete safety in my world or in my body. I had one client who was a publicly elected official and was unable to drive her car a block away from her house.

On the other hand I have had many rebirthees whose sense of unsafety led them to commit to social causes that addressed real issues and worked toward improving everyone's standard of living, worthwhile endeavors, but who never really made their life better because their true fear also stayed hidden behind the torch they carried. These may be in some instances even more difficult to address. Rather than the child being driven far underground or denied, here the child has gone into complicity with the adult to stay hidden, with many supporting defenses on both sides. The child agrees with the parental judgments about its helplessness and the futility in even addressing it and the adult has many socially reinforced judgments for not being "childish" or engaging in "useless rummaging through the past" when there are more important adult issues in which to attend. Unfortunately the fallacy that trying to banish fears and build a better society based on a shaky foundation and fear–laden principles never does provide true security personally or politically.

ABUNDANCE THEMES

During the first year of life we have obviously been safe enough to survive, but we are continually encountering the interplay between our inner needs and how the environment addresses them. There is not the sense of imminent hostility and threat for life here. At this stage there is an inconsistency experienced by the child, loving intentions on the one hand, but lack of follow through on the other. Or I may have some needs satisfied, material comfort, but a total lack in emotional presence. In any case, I conclude as a child that lack or its threat is integral to my daily experience. There is a profound sense of disappointment or abandonment associated with this experience. My child mind does not comprehend why I may get something today, but not tomorrow, or why someone else is getting it, but I am not. I learn to live in the state of uncertainty about what is really there for me, from milk and food, to attention and love, eventually to money or goods.

A frequent way I as a child adapt to this insecurity is to learn to fend for myself, grow up fast, at least in appearance. Those around me who themselves feel lacking are all too happy to reinforce my self care rather than my depending on them. I learn to play this game but with strings attached. My little child never really stops looking for that source which is abundant and keeps me secure about my needs being met. This may take the form of a fantasy lover to reassure me, the perfect job to insure my security, or the status that guarantees my abundance. All of these projects are doomed to psychological and emotional failure. No amount of goods or reassurances can truly reconcile my inner child's experience of having it, and then having it taken away. No insurance policy can change this consciousness of imminent abandonment. This search is an endless latching on to new hopes, followed by disappointment, depletion, and depression. Only I can change this theme with my inner child. It was I who bought the illusion that his abundance came from certain specific outside sources, e.g., Mother, Father, food, sex, money etc. When I did this I withdrew my love from this child and put my energy into securing these goods. This little girl or boy really needs to know that I am not judging her or him as inadequate and that I give up the game of accumulating enough friends, money etc. to make them worthwhile. This child needs to know that I love him or her for his or her intrinsic worth. This cannot be a phony declaration. They can tell. If I have bought these judgments, I cannot fake it. I must truly get back to that kind of person to person contact with the inner child I abandoned to adult pursuits before we can begin to establish mutual goals. (Goals must be inclusive of my child's needs as well as my adult's.) But my child is very sensitive to manipulations from adults: "Oh, you'll enjoy visiting Aunt Prunehilda." Too many times I have been guilty of ignoring my child's needs in favor of some adult pursuit. Upon first real contact with my inner child, I may encounter their anger, suspiciousness, or at best, cautiousness. If I am going to establish a true rapport, it is going to take a genuine devotion of time and energy.

My little child knows me better than anyone and can smell my manipulations a mile away. Later we will discuss ways to help establish a new level of mutual trust. I too must learn to trust that this child will not take over and run the show. Like those oppressed who didn't get their way for so long that now they will loot and pillage. This is real work and eminently worthwhile. For once my inner dialogue is honest and effective, once my parent and child have established trust and a working relationship, then the tremendous aliveness, spontaneity and creativity of the child is in concert with wisdom, guidance, and the ability to manifest of the adult. I am now in harmony within and this produces greater results that I could have imagined in my world. When I am not continually doubting myself, I project myself with greater certainty and inspire others to put their confidence in me. Others begin to recognize that I am the source of my own inner support. Not that I know all the answers nor that I am sufficient unto myself, but rather that even when I don't know the answers, I will not abandon myself. I will stick with me through my feelings and doubts. I will seek the sources, human and Divine, and stay with my search even through the illusion of immediate failure. I will not deny the ultimate power of internal unity, which is different from smugness, false complacency or egomania. It contains the humility in knowing that my inner dialogue will mean both my child and my adult will have something to let go of and something new to learn. This brings with it the uncertainty of not knowing it all, but the abundance of knowing that all the riches of the universe are there for us to discover and that we have a trusted loving partner on the journey.

In the end it is only me who can abandon my inner child. If someone walks away from me as perhaps my mother did at a time of my need, it is me who has the power to see this as her fear or lack as opposed to a statement about my true worth. Mistaking other's fear for my value and then closing down on me is the only real abandonment. In the face of someone else's judgment about me, going into agreement with it, then loving me less is the hurt my inner child still harbors. How many times have I done this? How many times can a child be rejected by a parent and still come back for love? Your child is there waiting for you to open your heart and arms and give the acceptance and guidance for which he or she has always hoped. No matter how many sources you may get approval from on the outside, no matter how much you may accumulate as a substitute for love, nothing can replace your open hearted taking in of the little one. You are the one for whom that child has longed. It will take seeing through the endless pursuits and goals you have set out for yourself. It does not necessarily mean you will turn aside from your goals or pursuits. In fact you may come at some of them with a new zest, because you are doing them together, you and your little one. Your little one knows that this voice will be heard; not necessarily that you will do everything asked, but that you will take it into account. Their needs for play and pleasure are headed. Ultimately no child wants to be left to run amok. They want your guidance and counsel. You will also develop more trust that your child will not be too selfish and unreasonable. Cooperation is the key and it starts with loving recognition and understanding. Are you willing to take the time and energy to breathe with and to recover that abandoned child? Your breath can provide the key to this door, the door to buried and lost parts of your full self.

CONTROL THEMES

As a child I gradually, during the later part of the first and second year of life, gain more mobility. I explore my environment – get into things. The response I get from my parents and significant others in my world, lets me know the degree of cooperation I can expect between my desire to take charge of my activities based on my natural curiosity and inner impulses and other's desires to set limits for me and restrict my action. Both are part of normal development. As a child I need guidance and I need freedom to learn at my own initiative. The harmony between inner and outer control that I experience sets the tone for my relationships being a dance of give and take based on mutual respect for each other's needs to the other end of the spectrum, a continual vying for power, control and dominance. I may experience this control as overpowering – the big people get their way. When I want something they do not want me to have, I am either physically removed, restrained or threatened. A more subtle but equally effective means of controlling me is through manipulation or seduction. My feelings are played upon "Mommy won't love you" or I may be blackmailed. One client told me his mother packed his bag and put him on the front steps for the people from the orphanage to come and get him when he did not behave.

I soon conclude under these conditions that all relationships are a power struggle. To lose power is to give others an advantage over you, like letting them know your weaknesses. It becomes imperative to hide my real feelings, act brave, tough, independent or at least indifferent. When my back is to the wall, however, then I resort to threat, attack, explosion, intimidation or some form of my own manipulation or seduction. The split this causes within me is between my child, who continually is on guard not to be shamed as a weakling or discovered to be truly incompetent, and my adult who must always be on top, one up, in charge. Fear and sadness are hidden within the child while anger and staying in charge become the domain of the adult. Neither of them are truly comfortable or trusting of each other. I live in a state of inner mistrust. I tend to push or bully myself around, rise above my feelings and run my life according to what will give me advantage, power or status rather than what will give my body comfort and pleasure. In fact, I am such a con artist that I convince myself that my pursuit of greater control is my true pleasure. My inner child is very sensitive to this and learns to resist often in indirect ways, bringing about failures that display the real state of affairs within my psyche – illness, accident, deals gone sour, rejections in relationships. I strive until it is impossible to keep up the pretense of always being in charge. This can precipitate a real collapse, repentance, breakthrough of terror, experience of shame or even violent retaliation.

If I listen to my inner dialogue I can hear the type of genuine cooperation and harmony that exists between the child within and the voice of my own inner parent. This voice had as its model your own parents and significant figures. Some may be nurturing and supportive. Others may be demanding and critical. Some may be sweet till they get compliance then the iron fist comes out of the velvet glove: "Ah, now that I am healthy again, it's back to work as usual," or "I'm glad I wasn't caught so now I can try to get away with it again."

I find it best in working with these voices not to try to obliterate them or deny their existence. Believe it or not they do ultimately want what they think is best for you and keep you independent. They are, however, misinformed and still operating in a fear based "dominated child" mode. To be sure you will consciously or unconsciously gravitate toward others who will reinforce this "survival of the fittest" mentality. It is our responsibility as the guides to our inner child to bring them into a world in which they are valued and respected, in which they can trust that it is not simply their guardedness or cleverness which will keep them on top. As a matter of fact the ability to let down and play or surrender to feelings safely and release them are the hidden treasures that the scared adult has never fully appreciated. Their inner mistrust can keep them always questioning the motives of others. Again what is happening within me will be directly reflected in my outside relations, especially those close to me.

I need to acknowledge the value of my inner child for his or her natural curiosity and ability to discover and learn from mistakes. When my child is always under the fear of criticism or ridicule, then they have to be right to "save face" at all times but hide a deeper sense of inferiority. I need to demonstrate a new interest and degree of tolerance. The payoff for this is a richness in my relationships that elicits the true love and cooperation my inner child has always wanted. This is the groundwork for a deeper foundation of true confidence – not in always being right but in being loved – cooperated with to live in world of harmony. Conscious breathing in the face of the fear of being controlled is the most powerful and direct way of reprogramming these deep–seated patterns. I learn to trust my own vulnerability rather than give my power away. If I ever do this in the presence of one other human being, usually starting with my rebirther, I can extend my self –trust even further. I can make more accurate judgments about people, whom to ask for what and with whom to share, because I am not judging them all through my fear. This does not mean I will automatically trust everyone with all my intimacies. On the contrary, I will be better able to see other's fears for what they are and not be caught up in them. I can be compassionate and giving, not gullible and naive nor closed and guarded. I have a true sense of my power and limits and am not continually looking to others to empower or validate me. My control comes from within and I am able to work and play in harmony with others without needing to dominate or be directed by them. Again, if I form this kind of relationship with my rebirth partner, I can do it with more and more people in my universe.

FREEDOM OF EXPRESSION THEMES

As I continue to mature during my second to third year of life, my range of expression expands. I go from simple coos of delight or wails of discomfort to more refined and discriminating human emotional expression. Each nuance of this expression, be it anger, sadness, fear or happiness, is noted and responded to by those around me. I am getting continual feedback from those in my environment about my forms of expression. Whether they want to or not, my family is letting me know how comfortable they are with each way I communicate. For example, if expressing any displeasure to mother is met with great hurt on her part or disproportionate anger on father's part, I learn to split off these unacceptable emotions from those that are met with approval. These constellations of feelings coalesce into the "good me" image versus the "bad me" image. This creates even further splits within me and between me and my inner child. My little boy or girl learns to use these two selves in different situations for different results. The "good me," whose feelings and behavior are accepted and reinforced, learns to perform before others, for example, while the "bad me," whose feelings and actions get disapproval, learns to hide and feel ashamed. Or in other cases the "bad me" gets more attention and predominates. Some families will label anger as unacceptable and glad as appropriate. Other families will encourage anger but punish fear. So there are any number of combinations and permutations to what a child is taught.

To complicate matters as a child I will consciously or unconsciously get different pictures from mother, father and other significant figures. Then as I enter the world of playmates or classmates, I continuously get signals about my appropriateness according to their families' cherished ways of being. My tendency will be to gravitate toward others with reactions similar to one or another of my parents or both. I say tendency because this is by no means an immutable law. Hopefully I also have a desire to explore differences and expand. As children and adults with strong inner children, however, the tendency to the familiar is quite strong if not immediately apparent. We often pride ourselves on having chosen a partner who is quite different than the last one who did not work out only to find after a while that they turned out to be "just the same." When, as a child, we were split on the feeling level, that child within us will forever seek to become whole again. We will do this by choosing partners, friends, work situations which recreate those original splitting dynamics in an effort to heal what has been a deep sense of incompletion and self judgment. It is that judgment that certain feelings were "bad" which causes me to distance from parts of myself. I will project these parts onto others, pick an angry mate for instance, in order to reconcile the discomfort with anger. This will almost never be a conscious choice. I think it was my mate's "forceful character" or "decisiveness." It will really be my inner child who is making many of my most important choices for reasons of which I am unaware.

The problem occurs as I attempt to have successful relations when I am not having a successful relation with my own inner child. I try to get my partner to make me happy (whole) either by changing them – so they are no longer angry, for example – or to get them to approve of my repressed feeling that I do not approve of myself – in this case tolerate my indirect or veiled anger. It never works. They cannot heal me, especially since they are most likely as equally occupied in trying to get me to heal them. Most relationships are being run by two inner children who have been split apart by (family) judgments about their self expression which they have adopted and continue to live out day by day. As long as neither party owns and heals his or her own child, the relationship repeatedly recreates situations of pain and alienation. They cannot possibly tell the emotional truth to each other that they have not told to themselves. These reenactments could lead to resolution if I turn a major portion of my attention inward, experience the truth of my own potential wholeness and forgive myself. Then I can stop trying to get from my partner what they cannot give me. This gives them the opportunity to do the same, the best gift I could ever give them. I can then express the truth to me which I have hidden behind self–judgment. This is not an intellectual process and is one of the most feared prospects that our inner child can face. If left only to my mind and its familiar excuses, I can talk my way out of ever facing the greatest fears of my little boy or girl. Taking myself back breath by breath and reclaiming through direct experience the depth and breadth of my true expression reunites the parts split through judgment. I experience the joy, power and freedom of my true wholehearted expression. This is life changing. This demonstrates to my child that I am willing to be whole in body, mind and spirit, not just read or think about it, but live it, to take a whole and complete breath again.

Ellie breathed into her feelings to come to an acceptance of them and to release the split that was controlling her relationships.

ELLIE, AGE 31
COMPUTER PROGRAMMER

I began rebirthing several years ago in hopes of dealing with pangs of jealousy that were filling my loving relationships. During my first rebirthing session, Kathy, my rebirther, told me the only way to let go of the jealous feelings was to accept them, feel them.

This idea was very new and uncomfortable at best. I had spent my life trying to control my feelings, not allowing myself to feel the emotions I had labeled as "not all–right." The turning point came for me many months later during a wet rebirth.

I was rebirthing with Kathy in her hot tub on a beautiful spring day. The session began with a discussion of letting go and surrendering to God. We talked about the uncertainty surrounding my career and my relationships.

Kathy then guided me through a meditation to help me relax and center myself. When I was ready, I put on the snorkel and mask and went underwater. My breathing was light and steady. I asked God for direction in my plans for the future. I concentrated on opening myself to my inner voice, but fear was blocking it.

I tried my usual techniques for pushing the feelings aside, affirming safety in the universe, trying to quiet the child inside of me. But my breathing was getting stronger and the fear only seemed to grow.

All else failing, I decided to allow the fear just to be, to accept it with love and gentleness. I was comforted by my inner voice telling me that I experienced great fear at birth and survived it.

The rebirth continued awhile longer as I integrated the wonderful peace of accepting all my feelings. A life–long struggle between my head and my heart was ending.

Since that day I have learned to embrace all my emotions. It is the key to my self–love. By accepting my feelings as they come up, they blend into my life instead of running it.

GENDER IDENTITY THEMES

As an infant I may have been called a "handsome little boy" or "darling little girl" from the onset. Identity as a male or female, however, takes on a whole new depth in the body as I begin to neurologically differentiate genital sensations and psychologically isolate and gain more control of genital feelings. This is taking place normally between the third and fifth year of life. At the same time, my understanding of environmental messages advances, and I pick up the cues more readily about what is acceptable expression of my sexual feelings. I also learn about what is considered appropriate male and female behavior. This is more than cultural stereotypes, it involves my parent's deep level responses to their own sexuality. They give messages to me on both the verbal and non verbal levels about their comfort and approval of my sexual expression and behaviors. This is where I begin to form my sexual identity on a strong experiential level.

As a parent I may wish to give more freedom to my child in their expression than I was allowed, so I give permissive verbal cues. When my child goes beyond what my real comfort level is, though, I may give more repressive non–verbal cues, for example, quickly changing the subject when the child asks about something embarrassing in company. Or on the other hand I may try to teach my child a fairly structured system of right and wrong about sexual expression, but myself behave in ways which contradict what I say. As a child I incorporate these conflicting messages and think I should be one way but act differently and feel guilty about it. This may very accurately portray my parent's own splits, even though I never directly saw them act inappropriately nor heard them talk about it. Their guilt and shame around their sexuality is communicated to me often more strongly and effectively without words. This is because the energy is picked up from their non–verbal cues and is repeated by my body out of my conscious awareness, making it all the harder to be under my conscious control. This is amplified when what is conscious is in direct opposition or denial of what I actually feel. This is true for both males and females.

I always pick up messages from both parents but often one will have more heavily charged messages for me than the other. When a father is threatened by any expression of assertion on his son's part and gives overpowering messages about his superiority and demeaning if not outright punishing responses to his son's assertion, the son learns for his own safety to act passively. The male child may learn to more comfortably adapt indirect ways of getting what he wants, employing sarcasm rather than expressing anger, having a veneer of politeness with a strong undercurrent of vengefulness. His sexual preference may be affected in this dynamic. He may be homosexual, heterosexual or bisexual. In all cases however, his personality is decidedly passive aggressive. His initiative in life is shaped by the fear engendered at a most formative period. He may be quite energetic and clever, he may compensate masterfully and in fact be very successful in his career. The hidden fear is often only exposed when there is a relationship crisis. The child has literally learned to hold his breath which is in opposition to our most primitive drive outside the womb, to take a breath. Consciously choosing to face this deep level of life choice can be accessed through opening up the breathing and uncovering the natural initiatives that were learned to be controlled through fear.

A similar situation prevails for the girl whose receptivity or sensitivity becomes a threat to the parent who cannot accept their own. A father, for example, may feel uncomfortable around open feminine energy and reinforce what he considers more safe and familiar male responses from his daughter. The girl soon compensates and gets rewarded by being aggressive and competitive. This becomes her self–image and may be particularly directed toward male figures. Again her sexual preference may or may not be altered in this dynamic, but most overtly her personality becomes hard–driving, argumentative, and oriented toward achieving and winning. Signs of softness or vulnerability are especially feared, because they tap into the early shame and rejecting messages that hurt so much. Again her breath is held from letting go completely. When she is able to release her breath and go past the fear that has held it tight, she can accept her vulnerability. She is then able to let down, truly be supported and at the same time know that she will take care of herself and not give her power away to someone else's judgments.

The sex drive is one of the most powerful and compelling in our human bodies. We cannot simply talk ourselves out of deep rooted postures when they are being reinforced in our bodies breath by breath. I can learn to breathe with my sexual energy and greatly enhance my self acceptance. I can learn to breathe during sexual expression and bring greater safety and pleasure to my body and my partner. I can learn to breathe with balance so that I can embrace both my masculine and feminine qualities.

Symbolic of the first creative act, conception and birth, was God's breathing life into the mud of Adam. We continue to make love to ourselves when we animate our bodies with the full breath of life, not the breath restricted by the fears of our ancestors. There are as many shades of maleness and femaleness as there are beings on our earth. To have the courage to discover my unique sexual identity means I must breathe beneath the surface of the images taught to me. I must find the means of expressing my maleness and femaleness, my yang and yin, my active and receptive qualities that are different than any other. I must breathe my body into its full aliveness and accept my own creative blend of being mother and father to my universe. Through this act of the divine lover, I am both the breather and the one breathed into. The sexual identity that emerges from this experience has no embarrassment and needs no excuses.

INTIMACY THEMES

Having established my level of safety in my body and in my world (pre & post birth), concluding how many resources are available to me (first year), deciding what level of harmony and control I have in my life (second year), adapting the freedom of expression that seems to work for me (second–fourth year), I have now established a sense of self. I have constructed a personality, if you will, that interacts with others in my life with varying degrees of intimacy. Significant experiences during my fourth to sixth year profoundly influence the conclusions I reach about my ability to have and keep intimate relationships. The personality I have created, of course, is just in it's emergent state but it already has an entire constellation of qualities, strengths and weaknesses that prepare me for dealing with the world. I may be fairly successful and have many skills in coping with challenges, yet never feel successful in opening my heart and sharing my deeper feelings much less maintain that quality of relationship over years. My inner child has concluded that vulnerability with my heart always leads to hurt and rejection and this gets borne out time and again. As an adult I may understand that it is not necessarily that way for everyone, but as good as I might be in resolving other people's problems, I seem to not have a clue as to why intimacy always eludes me. There is a scared and betrayed part of myself, which we are calling the inner child, who has learned a way of self–protection in the face of anticipated rejection that practically insures its happening.

I may have been the apple of Daddy's eye or Mama's special little one, until I began to relate to them as a sexual rather than a pre–sexual being. Having a newly established gender identity, able to focus and control more sensations in my genital area, I naturally experiment and explore with my newly developed body. This may pose the biggest threat yet to my parents, especially the parent who may become the object of my sexual attraction. I innocently may follow an instinctual sense of longing for the pleasure of arousal attached to that parent who also is someone I love. This additional sexual component to interaction with my parent may make them more uncomfortable than they can tolerate and lead to conscious or unconscious rejection. The little girl who could always sit on Daddy's lap, now may begin to feel genital sensation. This may be sensed by him either in his awareness or out of his awareness, but all of a sudden she is not as welcome or not welcome at all to sit on his lap. The sports page now has become more interesting than reading to her. Physical contact is now restricted, strained or eliminated. She may learn that she can get his attention by performing and may settle for this. In her heart, however, she feels betrayed. She was innocently open, loving, desirous and she was shut out. She could not distinguish his fear from her worth. She cannot deny the longing that keeps her searching for the lover who will accept her completely and heal the split between her heart and her genitals, between her love and her pleasure.

It seems like it was that male figure who caused the inner separation, so it must be a male figure, the mythical knight on the white horse, who can put her back together. Meanwhile she gets better and better at performing as a substitute. This performance is not just compensation. Genuine skills and talents are developed in dealing with the world. They have a hollow ring though, if they are not balanced by the ability to surrender to love, to let down to bodily pleasure, to experience a spontaneous inner union rather than having to make it happen. The adult takes over and learns to wall off and hold back because the little girl does not know how to express her rage at father without losing him altogether nor can she really get close and loving when she is so angry. This pattern repeats in future relationships and literally drives away the ones she loves. She may take solace in having relationships that satisfy her sensual desires – men who excite her but do not make a loving, long term partner – he may be already married or otherwise be unavailable. Or she may have men with whom she has a strong heart connection and respects but with whom she would never feel physically passionate.

Her little girl needs help in cracking the myth of the powerful male, and to reown the power of her own passion, to validate her sensuality from within, to express her rage in a way that unifies and affirms her and to answer her deep longing. This is a true rebirth of her child with her adult, a union of the vulnerable feeling one with the competent performing one. Rebirthing provides the framework to experience and own the passion in safety, to reprogram the old fear and conclusions. I can breathe in the face of both my rage and my desire without rejecting myself. This is the key, when I no longer reject me by shutting down my breath and closing off my heart, I can work through relationship challenges and own my power. I no longer confuse my partner's fear with my worth. I no longer need to reject myself and them before I get hurt again. I deal with my inner hurt responsibly within me which gives me the balance to give responsible messages to those outside me. Those who can handle my true power and passion will stay and form an equal, respectful, growing, exciting relationship – from friends to lovers. Those who are not ready to own their own power and passion will head for the hills. I no longer have to be the expert at picking the right people. When I am honest with myself and "be" the right person I no longer need to find the right person. They will self–select. I attract those who want to deal with me in my full potential and those who want to play rejection games get scared away. They see I am not interested in that style of relating. Just how I breathe fully with inner unity and confidence gives this message to my world. Only I can take the risk of opening up my breath and reclaiming the full aliveness of my inner child.

Patty reclaimed her power to bring herself out of darkness to go past her family patterns, especially with her father, and to be her own autonomous, creative person.

PATTY, AGE 33
SECRETARY

For the record I have not rebirthed many times. It's as though I have been afraid of it. My first rebirth was total darkness. I was not impressed with this so–called "re–birthing" process. I certainly could not understand what all the talk was about this breathing process.

What I failed to realize was this darkness had a message for me. I could not accept what I felt the darkness symbolized in my life.

So with much resistance, I forced myself into

another rebirthing session. Up to that point I had avoided and excused any possible opportunity to do so. I found myself at the Transformations Rebirth Training where it was reasonably hard to resist the opportunity.

My rebirthing began slowly. My resistance was high and I had the feeling I would never settle in. But after some concentrated effort I found myself embarking on a remarkable and joyous journey.

The process began in darkness. However, after awhile I saw some light. It was not clear and distinct, but soft and hazy. I then saw someone looking down directly at me. I could see the upper torso dressed in surgical garb and a plastic cap covering the hair. My immediate impression of this person was that I didn't like him or her. I'm not sure who it was – my feeling was that it was the doctor. The look on the person's face was drawn. The energy I felt was not happy or welcoming. Rather it was cold, impatient and certainly disinterested.

I then felt a hand placed on the small of my back. I tried to pull away physically and I felt myself pulling in. I struggled to avoid contact with this cold individual. I had the feeling of not liking where I was. I was definitely frightened.

I then switched from this scene to a feeling of floating along. I was continuing my journey. I remember my partner touching my forehead. This immediately brought to me memories of my mother. A surge of warmth and love overcame me. I felt very warm, content and at peace. Memories of my mother's love and support came to me. I then realized how much I did rely on those feelings and how much they do incorporate the core of me. I was very happy for my mother's gift to me.

I then switched again to the feelings of traveling

and floating. Only this time I was not in darkness, but I visualized the most beautiful color, a glorious shade of violet. It is hard to describe in words what the color looked like, but it was so beautiful to me that I don't think I will ever forget it. The closest thing I can describe it to is a hue that appears in the sky when there is a particularly beautiful sunset. There was so much light surrounding this color that I felt happy to be with it. In a sense, I was blown away by this image.

Then what suddenly appeared was an image of a door and a landing on a second level and I was looking down a flight of stairs to a door that led outdoors. This concrete staircase was enclosed in a building that was made of stone. This staircase was a part of a home. I knew immediately when I saw this image where I was. I was at my father's parents' home in Greece.

For me this was a good symbol. The image was in color and sharp and distinct in light. I knew that what I had to do was to walk down the flight of stairs and out the door. That symbolized to me my own personal freedom. It was symbolic of my break from my past and the family patterns especially created between my dad and I. I knew then that I could transcend the patterns and limitations of my family's dynamics. I knew that I could emerge as an autonomous, creative person and that I could live my life with my own clear free will.

I then again switched to this feeling of floating. I found myself traveling in grayness and becoming more aware of my surroundings. My partner whispered affirmations and I continued to breathe and enjoy the peacefulness and serenity of the process. I was feeling happy for what I had experienced. I continued to breathe and to take in fully my impressions and feelings. I knew that some important messages had come through for me and I wanted to assimilate them into my consciousness. I was happy for what was revealed to me.

I have been describing this stage of inner child development from the female point of view. The male child faces the very same split between his heart and his genitals during this period. In Western culture the male pattern may be even more obvious. It is even institutionalized in some countries as the Madonna/Prostitute Syndrome. Later in life the man is expected to have his wife whom he respects and defends to the hilt and his mistress to satisfy his "base or primitive needs." He may brag about the number of sexual conquests he has and never realize that his insatiable appetite stems from an inner split which keeps him also continually searching for that female that will satisfy him. No woman will ever be able to put his heart and his genitals back together as long as his little boy is locked away in terror of being hurt, of truly letting his heart open. He must have the courage to breathe past his fear and experience the anger and hurt around the original betrayal.

This betrayal to intimacy is not a single event that happened one day because a parent got scared of a child's sexuality or, more accurately, afraid of their response to their child's sexuality. The betrayal is a posture that I took as a child when I gave my power away to others in the face of my hurt. I closed down and decided "I will never be hurt again." It is an important developmental skill to learn how to discriminate and to what degree to open in relationships. The betrayal is recreated as I go on automatic pilot, so to speak, whenever a certain degree of closeness is achieved with another. I can no longer betray myself by recreating crises which keep me locked in hurt and distance, reinforcing my view that intimacy is too risky. I am short–changing myself. I can learn to breathe through these fears and reunite with this lost child. It is only my act of love to myself and my courage to follow through which will win the day. This starts with my next breath.

I have been describing these stages of growth in the life of the child as though they were fairly distinct steps along a developmental path. This is of course rather simplified. The truth is that we are continually reaching new conclusions about our safety, abundance, harmony, freedom, identity and intimacy. These stages overlap and recycle continuously. Being with children, especially those to whom you are close, restimulates the stages of your own growth and is a wonderful opportunity to grow yourself. You are both a teacher and a student with your children. It is humbling, nonetheless, to reexperience the dramatic powers of early feelings and conclusions we reached as children about ourselves and our world. This cannot be done on an intellectual basis because these postures we took toward life were physical, in the cells of our body. I cannot simply change my posture or habit because it is a good idea. I must also be inspired to go beyond my fears. I must breathe life into my own cells. I am then in a position to get the crowbar of consciousness in between my early feelings and my early conclusions about these feelings.

My goal is to reown the spontaneity and aliveness of my child while changing the negative and limiting conclusions that my child reached about these feelings. In other words, I can feel totally alive and be safe, abundant, harmonious, expressive, whole and intimate.

WHY WE DENY OUR INNER CHILD

The posture and conclusions I reached as a child still live within me inasmuch as I still run my life by them. This is the life of the inner child. To most, in fact to me, a number of years ago this was an interesting theory. I was not very impressed with it. I found out why – because it struck a cord of fear and defensiveness within me. The last thing I wanted to do was to return to my childhood, much less feel condemned to repeating childhood patterns. I had gone through my own therapy and personal growth groups years ago and certainly did not need to discount the health I had achieved through it. This is true. It is also true that there was more learning and healing to take place. My rebirthing and my rebirthing clients taught me this. As each one demonstrated the courage to go deeper into themselves without losing themselves, I saw how their inner child took on life and became more of a guide and teacher than I could have imagined. That child was able to show us experiences and uncover feelings that our conscious minds would take years to reach. By establishing a trusting contact with that child, a new level of inner cooperation was achieved and integration took place at an amazing rate. The first step was, however, often the most difficult.

One woman, I'll call her Pat, whom I had known for several years recoiled at the suggestion of visualizing her inner child. She was disgusted and repulsed when she finally did see her. She found nothing of merit in this "dirty sniveling little urchin." Pat gradually began to realize that all her judgments about her little girl were reflections of what she heard about her from her mother. She was terrorized by this woman, but also loved and needed her. Pat learned to identify with those judgments and keep the little girl hidden away in the attic. As she was brave enough to get closer, she realized how hurt and scared this little girl was. It was not appealing to reexperience any of this especially since that little girl had concluded she was powerless to do anything about her pain or her relationship with her mother. The best she could do was to keep her distance and stay out of her mother's way. When Pat grew up and adapted many of her mother's values, the little girl was following the same course and staying out of her way. It became obvious that there was as much mutual animosity and mistrust between Pat and her inner child as there was originally between Pat and her mother. They were afraid of each other. Indeed as strange as it may first sound, we end up treating our inner child much the same way we were treated by our parents until we consciously choose to do differently. Why don't we make obvious life affirming choices sooner? We do make very many and that is why we survived. But we have closed the door on many other scary choices that would take us beyond the survival level because

a) we are already getting by,
b) it is very scary and
c) we have not seen a model for doing it differently.

One of the biggest fears is how powerful that child really is. I do not want to be trapped in that little body again. This is where it is crucial to help the rebirthee see, hear and feel and intuit the child but not become the child so much that they split off from the adult and lose all the adult abilities to help out. The pull or temptation to collapse into the child and now, instead of being all adult, become all child is still having only half the picture. Pat was able to keep her dialogue progressing and to validate her little girl's fears, sadness and rage. She could do this because her adult promised to help keep her safe. If that little girl would have expressed her rage unassisted in her early environment, she might very possibly have been killed by her unstable mother. Even when the early environment is not this extreme our inner child fears emotional death or rejection and learns to stay closed. Pat eventually learned to hold, care for, play with and cherish this life within her and it directly translated into the quality of relationships she let into her life. As she became more loving within her, relationships outside her also became more safe and loving. She was able to invite others into her apartment which she had not been able to do before.

Pat was quite adept at visualization and after this experience even began teaching it to others. Some of us are not as visual with inner work and may need to hear or to feel or sense our inner child. Our inner child will know when we are willing to take the time and energy to find the best means of communication. Practice in one mode often helps the others. Regardless of the technique, that child is very sensitive to our intentions and will respond accordingly. I have worked with some rebirthees who have taken months to get the slightest inklings of their inner child and others who respond to it immediately. I must be respectful of this child's integrity. If my intention is to manipulate, control or boss around, this child will keep distant. My child has had plenty of adult types telling him what to do and controlling him "for his own good." Our inner child can read through our ploys to gain control even when we have convinced ourselves that we are sincerely seeking an equal relationship.

BEGINNING THE DIALOGUE

I will often ask rebirthees to direct questions and make suggestions and ask for information to their inner child. After some success the rebirthee becomes adept at their own dialogue. In the beginning, though, I must learn to truly listen to the messages and cues from this child. There may be silence and non–responsiveness. I may have to trust my intuition as to what this is about. When I make a suggestion, e.g., can you visualize letting your father come into the room, and I get a "no," I must hear it and honor it. This builds up a record of trust, so the child knows its feelings will be heard and it will not be overwhelmed. Eventually each rebirthee learns his or her own special way to connect with the inner child using breath as the door opener.

Like any relationship, it takes practice and commitment. I cannot reconnect with my child, have a grand reunion then leave and not speak again for weeks, months or even years. I recommend a daily breathing practice during which I may communicate with my inner child. This child helps me more than I could have ever imagined, not just with releasing the past, but enriching the present. This child will candidly and directly let you know what you really feel and want on the deepest levels. When the child and adult are working together, they have the best of both worlds, playfulness and productivity. Putting up a picture of yourself as a child can also help stimulate your dialogue as well as having something around you daily, something to which your child responds, like a stuffed animal or a favorite toy. Overcoming your adult embarrassment will also be a sign to your inner child that you have truly invited them back into your life.

A simple way to begin your dialogue is to ask three questions as you direct your attention inwards: "Where is Little (the name you were called as a child)?" "What do you feel?" "What do you need and want?" Pause after each question and wait for an inner response. What you hear will most likely be direct, childlike and to the point. You do not have to grant your inner child's every request. This is a real dialogue not a demand. Your attention and consideration is most important. Stay with the conversation until you are both satisfied. As you gain mutual trust and respect, the creativity and profundity of your dialogue will increase. Your child will become your Divine Infant and lead you to the source of great wisdom.

I do this dialogue morning and evening. My child helps me plan my day and prioritize what is really important to me. My child is the best consultant that I could have. The time I take to spend with him is not only centering and gratifying, it is also "cost effective." My child helps me see what is truly purposeful and to let go of the rest. I am much too busy to not check in daily with this source of guidance.

THE INNER PARENT

Much emphasis has been put on inner child work recently and this is great. Not much is said though about the inner parent. That part of us who gives messages of guidance and direction to the child, who has been modeled after our birth parents, often gets as bad a name as we originally wanted to give our parents when they made unpopular decisions. Our "inner parent" needs as much help and assistance as our inner child does. The old parenting model has been that we should know it all, have all the right answers, be perfect. Laboring under this kind of strain is what makes us dictators and tyrants to our inner child. Our inner parent must know that perfection is inhibitory to a genuine dialogue. The parent need not be perfect, just willing to be there, listen to and give guidance by sharing the benefit of her or his experience. The child needs to know that the parent will not abandon him or her even when there is a disagreement. Both need to be heard. The parent needs to know that the child will not always be willful, stubborn or rebellious. Both need to believe in the process little by little, and come to believe in themselves as well as each other. The parent abandons the child by refusing to hear or take the child's needs and wants into account. Not that the parent will always do what the child wants, but that the parent is willing to work toward the good for all. At times the child may need to express irrationally. This is good for all that the irrational component of self is expressed and the child is often best at doing it. The child ultimately does not want, however, to take over and run amok without any guidance or limit setting from the parent. This is a false sense of power that leads to loneliness and frustration. Our inner parent needs support in giving guidelines that are not too rigid nor too porous. This is especially difficult when, again, we have had no model of this. The rebirther can provide an example of such parenting. This is only one source of modeling though it can be an important one. I believe there is a deeper sense of inner guidance that goes beyond all the external models.

Once there has been a successful encounter between the inner child and inner parent, something unique can happen. The noise of the battle subsides even though it may have been a cold war. I begin to realize that I am not trapped in either the child or parent roles. I am able to shuttle between these two with increasingly greater ease. But where am I when I am being neither one? This opens the door to an experience of me that is akin what has been called in some traditions "The Witness." This is the presence that I am who is not on either side of the dialogue. As this presence I am invested in not one nor the other winning, but in the dialogue leading me to greater resolution, effectiveness and serenity.

Through understanding and courage on both sides of my dialogue I can reach forgiveness. Forgiveness is the key to going beyond the stuckness in our inner dialogue and the addictive behavior attached to the stuckness as Diane discovered.

DIANE, AGE 31
PROGRAM ANALYST

At the Pleasure Intensive, I had a significant rebirth with Rick. In it, I had conversations with my parents. I remember asking my mother over and over again, "why do you drink?" and not being satisfied with any of her answers. Then I realized that she abused alcohol for the same reasons that I have had compulsive eating problems. I think it was the first time that I really understood why someone would want to abuse alcohol. There was some real forgiveness that took place, and I told both my mother and my father that I love them. And I told Diane that I love her, too.

Experience of the Witness state is rare at first, but is such an all encompassing non–judgmental expression of love that it is very compelling and motivating, life changing. Once I admit this way of being, many of my old investments in proving my child point of view or my adult point of view as right lose their steam. In a way I have less to prove and more to enjoy. This also directly affects my outer dialogues. My relationships become less contentious, less of a struggle and more of a mutual sharing. They are not boring by any stretch of the imagination. Full creative interplay is set free by resolution of warring factions. This position of witness is often the experience of my being after the completion of a rebirthing. Each time I achieve this state it reinforces my ability to do so and to access this non–partial wisdom even at times when I get caught up in my drama.

The first step to this freedom is rebirthing my inner child, reowning the truth that goes beyond all my present excuses for why my life cannot work better, either self–blame or blame of others. I must come back to that original breath of aliveness and see with the awe and wonder of a new–born. Each one of us has this inner child, each one of us can bring that child home to our hearts.

AFFIRMATIONS FOR THE INNER CHILD

Affirmations are positive messages used to replace old negative or limiting conclusions reached as children. They are not "brain washing" because I choose them voluntarily and say them lovingly. They are "brain cleaning" in that they assist me to throw away my old mental tapes or at least replace them more and more with messages that unite and enliven me.

Affirmations can be said, written or listened to in the first person, "I am safe," second person, "You are safe, Jim" or third person "Jim is safe." Experiment and play with the modes that work best for you. Different ones may work better at different times or for different themes. It is best to breathe fully when I say them.

SAFETY

I AM SAFE.

MY UNIVERSE IS A SAFE PLACE.

I AM WELCOME AND WANTED HERE.

ABUNDANCE

THERE IS AN INFINITE SOURCE WITHIN ME.

I LIVE IN A WORLD OF ABUNDANCE.

I WILL LOVE AND CARE FOR ME ALWAYS.

CONTROL/HARMONY

I AM SAFE AS I LET DOWN AND PLAY.

I AM SUPPORTED BY LOVING PEOPLE.

MY VULNERABILITY IS PART OF MY STRENGTH.

FREEDOM AND EXPRESSION

EXPRESSING MY FEELINGS OPENHEARTEDLY IS EASIER AND EASIER.

ALL MY FEELINGS ARE HEALTHY.

I GET CLOSER TO OTHERS AS I SHARE MY TRUE FEELINGS.

GENDER IDENTITY

MY SEXUALITY IS A BEAUTIFUL PART OF MY ALIVENESS.

I LIKE THE WAY I AM A MAN (WOMAN).

I AM A PERFECT BALANCE OF MALE AND FEMALE.

INTIMACY

I SHARE MY HEART MORE SAFELY BECAUSE I RELEASE MY HURT AND FEAR MORE FREELY.

I SURRENDER TO LOVE AND WIN.

I BREATHE IN LOVE AND SEXUAL FULFILLMENT.

CHAPTER FOUR

REBIRTHING YOURSELF

My goal as a rebirther or breath guide is to assist each rebirthee to, as soon as possible, engage in the process on one's own. Each rebirther is a student of the process who assists others by observing the healing, pointing it out and getting out of the way to let it happen. All healing is self–healing and is assisted by the medium of love. The rebirther presents a model for the creation of this medium.

HAVING A VISION OF WHOLENESS

Rebirthing operates directly from the essence of all forms of healing – the pure loving vision of wholeness and the intention to release any illusion to the contrary. To touch and to be whole requires trust and faith in the power within. When there is a shared vision on the part of the rebirther and rebirthee, a vision of the truth of both parties and the loving bond between them, the healing position is very strong. To rebirth myself I learn how to breathe and maintain this vision of my wholeness. This puts the spirit of creation into practice. I fully own my unity with the prime mover in my existence, the one who is breathing the life into my body.

To rebirth myself I must be willing to increase my awareness of each of my life intentions. Since what I presently have in my life is the product of my creative thought, I must be willing not only to accept responsibility for my creation, but also to see my loving intentions and how they have gotten distorted by limiting beliefs along the way. I cannot simply decide to slap new intentions for health, happiness and peace on the top of old fears that I maintain. This produces a shaky foundation for the new life I am wanting to build. I must release the old feelings and negative conclusions which surround me and weigh me down. To hold on to the old while I try to embrace the new creates struggle. Keeping the old leaves little room for the new. My birth scene is a symbol of the former structure in which I lived. My rebirthing is a reframing of the mental and emotional structures within which I now live.

A DAILY PRACTICE

There is a part of me that would like my new house to be constructed and for my moving in to take place instantaneously. Designing, building and maintaining a new residence, however, is a process that requires my own time and pace. I am the architect, the builder and the janitor of my mind. Every rebirthing session requires that I plan and implement new patterns of self–affirming thought as well as cleaning up old messy ones. With each breathing cycle I set out an affirming intention. Then as I breathe I must use the tools of creative thought while I clear and release negative thoughts and bound emotion. I sharpen my skills in each area by practice. A daily practice of self–affirming breathing is what leads to mastery in all areas. To wait for a crisis in order to test my skills forestalls my development.

The development of a regular affirmative breathing routine lets me see through the veil of boredom in everyday events. I experience the dynamic energies of the universe at play inside and outside of my body. The peace I reach through this practice is not a static, frozen state. True peace is the state of dynamic equilibrium that embraces all forms of chaos. When I think I am in chaos, it is because I am fixed in one small portion of the truth which does not make sense. Isolation never does. I need to give myself the breathing space to see a broader picture and then I see how my present situation fits into a greater harmony. Daily affirmative breathing develops my ability to get unstuck, go beyond apparent chaos, and experience the truth, simplicity and love around me.

Bob has established his own form of daily breath practice and gone beyond the search for the dramatic "quick fix" to the peace and joy of breath by breath awareness.

BOB, AGE 32
THERAPIST

My most significant rebirth occurs daily. How fortunate! For me, this is an extremely important realization and it has been a long time coming. I'd like to explain.

Much of my life, I have been addicted to what I thought of as "getting high." I'd make myself feel tense and restless while I waited for that one Grand Cosmic Experience which, I hoped, would change my life forever, eliminating doubt, fear, confusion, pain, and anything else I deemed unacceptable. I've looked for this in drugs, booze, sex, relationships, religion, personal growth seminars, you name it. My quest for the Ultimate High. I even thought lying down and breathing would give me this! Note: all these were things or experiences I thought would give me what I needed. As though it were not up to me!

In my seeking, I have had incredible, mind–blowing experiences, and clung to them crying, "Wait! Don't let me return to the 'real world' of responsibility and change!" Don't, in short, cast me out of the apparent safety of the womb.

I've given up my search for the Perfect Permanent Experience. More than ever, I allow myself to enjoy each breath, each expression of affection, every moment of peace and joyfulness. These are things I can experience every day, along with my familiar doubts, fears, and aches. I enjoy living so much more then when I felt as though I were cruising on remote control. I prefer daily contentment to Major Intensities followed by Crashing Disappointments. I now live for the simple, direct pleasures of breathing deeply, loving and being loved, stretching and moving my body, beautiful thoughts and sights and sounds. By opening myself to the abundance which surrounds me and flows through me, I daily experience Rebirth.

I am enormously grateful.

CHOOSING A REBIRTHER

Most people at the onset use the assistance of a rebirther when learning how to rebirth themselves. I recommend this and also emphasize that the choice of your rebirther is an integral part of your rebirthing. Having a level of confidence and trust in the rebirther you choose is important in your self–care. It is OK to ask questions to get a good feel for how the rebirther approaches the process. It is equally important to remember that you are ultimately responsible for your outcome and you are engaging the rebirther to assist you in achieving positive results.

THE REBIRTHING SESSION

Rebirthers or breath guides have developed many and varied styles of conducting rebirthing sessions. I will present what I think are common denominators of successful rebirthing sessions.

People come to me for rebirthing ordinarily at times of life transition. During life transitions people often display their familiar style of going from one state of life to another (as symbolized by their birth drama). Some struggle and resist, others focus on the lack of support they seem to be getting from the authorities, some deaden themselves and are not emotionally present, others feel stuck for long periods or see themselves as inadequate for the task. All these are old limiting conclusions about themselves and their world and will directly effect their present level of growth unless addressed. The fact is they all made it and will make it again, but they can learn to do it with significantly greater ease and pleasure. In fact, their very inner prompting for growth is the opportunity to clean house and eliminate old baggage.

HAVING A CLEAR INTENTION

The first order of business in a rebirthing session is to be clear about your intention for engaging in the process. If I am unclear about what I want, I will be unclear about what I got. I will not personally rebirth with anyone unless I feel clear about their loving intention. The rebirth process increases available life energy in the body. To simply have more energy to invest in old patterns is pointless and painful. Gaining this clarity of intention may be brief and intuitive or it may take several hours or even sessions of verbal investigation. I may sense a clarity of the spirit which brought the rebirthee in even though his or her mind is confused. Some rebirthers operate just with their intuition. I like to have the rebirthee's intention verbalized to help bring the mind more fully into alignment with what we are doing in the body.

In my personal practice as a rebirther I usually take at least an hour with a new rebirthee in understanding this person's major life themes. This often involves an overview of family systems and significant life events including birth, schooling, dating, etc. In this life review we do not just collect information, but begin to sift out recurrent personal themes, to understand the individual's life purpose and to reframe some of the limiting beliefs as well as to inspire and reinforce the person's strength and positive directions. We gain greater clarity on the purpose and value of rebirthing now in the rebirthee's life.

REBIRTHING IN BODY

At this point in a session I will explain the breathing process. I note that rebirthing takes place in the body, mind and spirit. On the physical level it relieves tension by melting energy blocks. I use the simple analogy of the body being a garden hose with the breath being the water flowing through. Rebirthing turns up the amount of flow of air. As in a Walt Disney cartoon, when there is something inside the hose blocking the water's flow, it bulges out until the block releases and the energy whooshes out. As simplistic as it seems, this is often the experience on the physical level. As the rebirthee breathes, there is a build–up of energy until their resistance releases and then there is a feeling of intense flow and a sense of being cleansed and refreshed. Sometimes this brings more light and clarity than the person has ever remembered.

Don stayed with his breath through intense physical sensation and pain in his body that had blocked his experience of freedom and pleasure most of his life.

DON, AGE 54
UNIVERSITY PROFESSOR

This was my second, formal, guided breathing, done with Jim Morningstar. It's selection is almost random because each rebirthing has contributed something significant and powerful, and which I sense is greater beyond my conscious awareness. What was conscious is reported as follows:

Jim asked what I wanted and my answer was to contact my soul. To be the human being I am capable of being. Breathing came easily though slightly painfully – not so much of dryness as first time, though for a moment I had a lot of swallowing and throat moistening to indulge in – pain may be from cigar smoking that I told Jim about – yawns came past, within 5 minutes – great yawns – prolonged – then came up a resurgence of those deep feelings, this time definitely of sadness – I spoke to Jim in allowable snatches of this sadness. He quietly encouraged me to proceed with this up swelling – I was surely going to – sadness is something I have gotten into in my life, especially in very sensitive moments involving deep compassion for others or even myself – a part of me knows this sadness over my foolish blindness, ignorance, errant ways. It felt very good, this need to cry, gasping, gulping emotionality, however powerful the expression of feeling pouring out – Ah, it was good! Then came, of all surprises, the "electrical" energy – full upper body including torso, arms and especially face were vibrating with immense tingling of energy – Phew! – Not painful, but not pleasant either.

I told Jim I felt that I was plugged into a 110V. outlet. He acknowledged – This lasted through–out rest of the session. I prayed "please, please, let me be a part of you, please, accept me into you, come into me, let me bring you into me, into this planet," or words to that effect. Peaks were leveling off, but vibrations were immense. I found it easier to talk to Jim. Something I guess I enjoy doing – it is out of a good trust and I guess an eagerness to share with a human being who is so willing to share himself with me.

I noticed an almost painful tightening in my solar plexus – gut – back (lower) was tightened up and aching, too – told Jim – began to undulate hips to loosen up back muscles – after awhile in that transverbal knowing without words way, I recognized a complex of associations, both physical and emotional and told Jim in a minimum of words with great merriment! Pelvic thrusting was sexual–like – gut and back tightening were directly linked – years of anxiety had surely migrated their tension to lower back. Lower back tension loosened up and allowed my gut to be free, loose, at ease. Jim later added that a need to love with its fulfillment would certainly add to this healing. When he handed me this session's list of affirma-

tions, Jim pointed out the importance of the word "pleasure." He commented on my tendency to continue working when I could have come out. I knew what he meant – these sessions are both pleasure and privilege. Vibrations hung in even after eyes opened and during discussion and reading affirmations – I asked, "was I really breathing?" "Yes," he said, to my continued amazement. I just didn't recall. Again the warmth, love, fellowship, sense of sacredness of within myself, Jim, his home, his family, Joyce, my friends, our planet, all of us schluck–heads! Great peace, good humor, God–sent courage renewed. We talked, I don't recall of what fully now. Oh, breathing – pelvic thrusting – tension release – love – all related! Stood up – really dizzy and off balance – OK, and balance returned fast. We did discuss how clusters of people were growing and developing in a quilt–work pattern and inevitably join hands more and more so in recovering our world with a new world view, ethic, attitude, consciousness – I left with new–found breath, peace, wholeness, belonging!

REBIRTHING IN MIND

On the mental level there is a parallel clearing. The body and the mind are two sides of the same coin. Physical constriction is the reflection of limiting beliefs in the mind. Some rebirthees connect the physical and the mental very consciously, actually seeing while they breathe some of the life events up to and including their own birth. It was during these events that they froze their energy and reached negative conclusions about themselves and their world. In this conflict between their original belief in their lovability and the illusion to the contrary (perhaps mother left the room when they wanted attention), they chose some lesser image of themselves and held on to the feelings (hurt or sadness or fear). The tension that it takes to maintain a permanent state of fear fades from my awareness and I come to accept that this tension is my ordinary physical state and that being rejectable is my normal mental condition. These attitudes continue to exert influence until I have the courage to face them and redecide about their truth. I say courage because who wants to reopen old wounds just to feel bad once more? I must have faith on some level of my being that my old negative conclusions are erroneous. In most cases this faith and courage transforms that held energy, either instantaneously or within a few minutes, to free flowing energy which is experienced as light and pleasurable. There is no fooling the mind and body about this. If there were not some risk involved, I would have released and felt better years ago. Either I have gained in confidence enough or believe that my back is to the wall and I have little to lose and that with the aid of the rebirther, I am now willing to challenge the fear that has held me back. Originally this holding was a self–protective measure from experiencing what I thought was life threatening. The holding had a loving intention behind it. Now, however, holding my life energies back no longer serves me and I am willing to operate with less fear. In a few cases the holding takes a bit longer to release, rarely longer than one half an hour. Indeed it is possible to hold on longer, but given the opportunity, both the body and the mind seek freedom.

In the mind this freedom means a more positive sense about myself, acceptance of beliefs that support me and clarity about my priorities. Many people who survive a life–threatening illness or accident change the way they treat themselves and pay more attention to the love that surrounds them. Rebirthing is a direct route back to your priorities without having to recreate the drama of mortal danger. I believe on some level we orchestrate those "mortal dangers" to try to shock ourselves out of our frozen states. I see people escalating these shocks until they release the truth of their inner safety. Sometimes they decide not to fully accept it in this lifetime. To rebirth is to decide to get it now.

Not all of my mental realizations come in the form of remembered life events. In fact, a relatively small amount do for most rebirthees. The change in mental attitude, though, is quite clear. Continued practice with the affirming breath is what helps maintain this clarity through all the life events which follow the rebirthing session. At the end of the rebirthing sessions I facilitate, I ordinarily write a page of affirmations specifically for helping to maintain the rebirthee's clarity.

REBIRTHING IN SPIRIT

On the spiritual level, rebirthing is attunement to the divine spirit within me. It means being at one with the author of my existence. It puts me back in the driver's seat of my life, rather than in the back seat wondering where I am being taken next. I sense a great deal of spiritual guidance and support being given to rebirthees while they are in session. To rebirth with a positive loving intention is to open myself to the positive supportive energies of the universe. First of all, it is crucial that the rebirthees be aware that it is they who are in the driver's seat and who are responsible for their outcome in the session. As a rebirther I am with them every breath. I give feedback and suggestion along the way and am there to support them 100%. The rebirthees, however, are the ones who take that feedback and suggestion and use it in the way that is just right for them. For the rebirthees to "give their power away" – see the rebirther as the one controlling them – is to recreate the birth drama in which the doctor was blamed for the outcome. People spend their entire lives trying to work out their relationships with doctors and other authorities whom they view as not giving them what they need. I must dissolve the illusion that the doctor is the source of what I need. I must find the healer within me. The rebirthing is most effective when both the rebirthee and rebirther take total responsibility for themselves and share with each other from their fullness. This does not mean that either know exactly what is going to happen or how. Responsibility means being committed to use whatever happens toward self–acceptance without blaming the self or the other along the way. If either party does no sense this responsibility from themselves or the other, they will usually find some good reason not to proceed until this is clear.

Secondly, it is important that the rebirthee understand that the goal of the session is for release, lightness and the pleasure that comes from harmony inside and out. Regardless of all the past drama or present challenges, the point is not to wallow in them or trump them up, but rather to keep a clear focus on the state of light and peace. Anything else is a distraction.

BEGINNING THE SESSION

After briefly explaining the rebirthing process and answering any questions the rebirthee may have, we are ready to begin the breathing process. I usually recommend that the rebirthee use the lavatory to clear the bladder immediately before the breathing to avoid discomfort when the body relaxes completely in the session.

There often is a fair degree of expectation on the part of the rebirthee before the breathing. The rebirthees have put themselves in the position of willingness to face their innermost fears. Some anticipation is quite natural. In most cases the rebirthees, know it or not, have been experiencing and dealing with this fear from the moment they made the commitment to be rebirthed. By the time they arrive at the session and get ready to rebirth, they have already processed a great deal of what it takes to begin life anew. This period is akin to the prenatal and they may have even reenacted some of their prenatal experience before the rebirthing. It is helpful to recognize this and acknowledge the courage and intention it takes even to get that far.

The simple breathing technique can be done anywhere and in any position, but most find it helpful to first learn the process while lying down. In my office I have a foam mat to lie on and a comforter which is ready for the rebirthees to use if their body gets chilly during the process. Once the rebirthee is lying down I give the final breathing instructions.

CONNECTED BREATHING

I ask the rebirthee to maintain a connected breathing rhythm, pulling the air in through the mouth into the heart region, then relaxing immediately, exhaling through the mouth. There is no pause between inhale and exhale. The eyes ordinarily remain closed and the pace is vigorous, but not rushed. The rebirthees adjust their body and mind to keep a relaxed open state while continuing their breathing fully and freely. The mental focus starts with regulating the breathing openly and trusting in the inner healing process. I ask the rebirthees to state or reaffirm their intention for the rebirthing and begin to establish a breathing rhythm that they can maintain for approximately 50–60 minutes. As a rebirthee, the first few minutes of my session are usually occupied with getting comfortable both to my breathing rhythm and to the setting in which I am breathing. I adjust my body and mind to letting go and being present to whatever happens. My attitude is not overly heavy and ponderous, nor is it flip or distractible. I can take myself seriously and lightly at the same time. I begin the process immediately and display my current state in the first few minutes of breathing. If my breath feels too forced, I ease off. If it feels too shallow, I deepen it. Here is where the feedback of the rebirther is important. Usually the rebirther will watch me establish my rhythm before making suggestions. What may seem a good pace to me, though, may reveal dramatic blockage and holding patterns to the rebirther. I take the rebirther's suggestions and fit them to my body.

BREATHING THROUGH FEELINGS

In adjusting my breath to my body sensations, attitudes and feelings may surface. I may, for example, have a flash of anger at the rebirther for expecting me to "do the impossible." At this point I can turn the anger inward and feel guilty for not fitting the expectations of others or I may resent the rebirther and begin to either resist or withdraw. This instantaneous flash may be very obvious or so subtle that I repress it like most uncomfortable interactions. If I repress it, any breathing will be hampered. NOTICE!! Each moment of breathing either reinforces old patterns or helps to release them. By catching my reaction and investing my anger energy in a worthwhile target, e.g., my fear of going beyond my limits, I can reown energy and experience greater freedom and aliveness. I may have had a lifelong pattern of being angry at authorities and using this as an excuse for not going beyond my limits and gaining success in my life. I may even have been in therapy and have analyzed and understood this pattern. What I may not have done, however, is to break out of the pattern and feel the pleasure and strength that comes from taking control of my life. The simple act of taking a full, free breath and supporting myself when I get this old flash of anger, can be more valuable than years of talking about it and understanding it. I directly experience my control over an energy that formerly always produced separation and restriction. This is the immediate and direct healing power of rebirthing. Granted, this is a minor example. I could have chosen a flash of fear or sadness or any feeling that has led to one of my regular repressive reactions. The model for self– support through breathing into and through the feeling rather than holding and thinking about it is valid in every case. The instructions during the entire session are simple and redundant: keep breathing openly. Talking about my awareness at this point would forestall the healing. If my holding patterns were so ingrained that they escape any awareness, the breathing process will bring them out. They will magnify with each breath until they become obvious even to me. They will produce imbalance and discomfort which I will register as unpleasant sensation and the desire to leave and stop breathing fully.

Karen exemplifies the courage it takes to trust one's breath in the midst of whatever emerges during the process and the willingness to release any pain en route to the light.

KAREN, AGE 42
NURSE

On November 1, 1983, I went through my second rebirthing with Jim. My neck, jaws, mouth were a new addition to my hands and feet in tetany. As the fear, anger, rage surfaced I became aware of a calm warm source of strength. It seemed necessary to clear out the negatives to get in touch with that inner source. As I struggled with the waves of negatives that seemed intolerable I was aware of the source of inner strength nurturing me. I sought the source and was amazed at the speed with which it pushed out "the garbage." To touch it was to be instantly encompassed by white light. Every cell was "breathed full" of love, peace, joy. In this state I was aware that "I Am." Cradled in this calm warmth was to experience true bliss.. I now know the meaning of the poem I copied down in 1978.

> *"Think of stepping on shore and finding it heaven;*
> *Taking hold of a hand and finding it Gods';*
> *Breathing new air and finding it celestial;*
> *Feeling invigorated and finding it immortality;*
> *Of passing through a tempest to a new and*
> *unknown ground;*
> *Of waking up well and happy and finding it*
> *HOME."*

From
"Each New Day" by Corrie Ten Boom
a daily devotional book

Each rebirthing breath is directed toward light and aliveness in my body. What happens during a session is as varied as are the life stories on the face of the earth The principle in each case, though, is similar. Whatever I am doing to restrict the total experience of my aliveness will surface when I breathe fully and freely with loving intention.

The style of my breathing will reflect the style of how I put my energy into my life. I may be great at taking in, but tense in letting out or vice versa. I may only breathe energy into my gut but be frozen in my heart area – willing to guts my way through life but not really putting my heart into it. I may be alive and vibrant in my upper body, but lifeless in my lower body. Again, the patterns are many. The opportunity presented in the rebirthing session is not just to see them, but to immediately do something about them.

CHANGING YOUR THOUGHTS

I gravitated to rebirthing because I was an expert at thinking and talking; so much so that I could talk myself in or out of just about anything. Rebirthing presented me with the challenge that I could not talk my way out of. I had to take action – release my holding and come home to the truth of who I am. During one of my beginning rebirthings, suddenly began to feel nauseous to the point where it really concerned me. I related this to my rebirther. She instructed me to change the thought I was having about the feeling and to breathe into it. I was insulted by this simplistic approach to what I considered to be dire stress on my part. Internally I was saying "Lady, I'm really sick. I don't need any philosophy lessons. I need a bucket!"

However, I was so far into the process (and unable to move easily) that I decided to humor her and actually try her advice as a last resort. I began to affirm that I was releasing illness from my body with each breath and to relax into the sensations. Within a minute or so the uncomfortable feelings had dissipated. I was shocked. No amount of theorizing or philosophizing was as powerful for me as this direct experience of the effect of my creative loving intention. Not every symptom may clear this easily, but the principle is always the same. True, I at times kicked and fought against the rebirthing process, but I am eternally grateful for the results.

ADJUSTING THE RHYTHM

The first part of the session, then, involves getting comfortable, finding my breathing rhythm and learning to stay with the breathing process. I usually recommend starting with mouth breathing, especially during the first ten sessions. Once a rebirthee has mastered, to a certain degree, the heart–clearing, emotional energies that this sympathetic nervous system activating breath generates, then the type of breathing can be selected as a conscious choice rather than as an avoidance of feeling. If, however, the mouth breathing is too uncomfortable immediately, I may start with nose breathing. The goal is breathing free to full aliveness with the least struggle along the way. All general rules can be waived in favor of a more direct intuitive route. Each person's path is different.

After establishing a regular, open breathing rhythm, the rebirthee may start to get a dry mouth, or feel dizzy or tingling in the limbs and hyperventilation symptoms. It is here that the breath must be adjusted, often more relaxation on the exhale. The mind must also be reminded of its safety in the face of the physical associations with fear. As I relax both my body and mind, these surface symptoms disappear and I am actually able to breathe more fully than my old holding pattern would have allowed. In some cases the holding patterns are so severe that the body stiffens and contorts. I have seen the most intense physical blockage release immediately, however, when the rebirthees let go of their fear or negative thoughts. Sometimes the holding pattern releases more gradually, but in either case the body senses and rejoices in its newfound freedom.

In most cases the middle portion of a rebirthing session involves a breath by breath release of limitation and increase of aliveness. There can be a conscious review of life events up to and including my birth, or a more meditative, non cognitive releasing. The rebirther is there to assist the rebirthees in learning to direct and play with their newly opened energy flow. This usually builds to a crescendo, then naturally subsides when holding patterns are released. Generally, initial rebirthing sessions deal more with the clearing of old blockage. Later on, more advanced rebirthing sessions involve conscious energizing, exploring, learning and creating with life energy.

RELEASING RESISTANCE

If I have a blockage in the way of this natural breathing cycle, there will be some disruption of my breathing rhythm. This resistance to full and free breathing is a reflection of the way that I impede the experience of pleasure and achievement of my goals in life. To breathe through this fear in rebirthing is to open the door to doing the same in all of my life. Sometimes the resistance has been so great that the potential rebirthee has never gotten to the session. In the session, however, there are innumerable ways of distracting and interrupting my natural drive toward completion. I may, for instance, alter my breathing rhythm every time I start to feel a building of energy – I'm afraid of losing control. I may over–control my breathing and become mechanical – using will with no heart in it. I may start talking, report my experience rather than stay in it, or begin to dramatize through physical movements. Both verbalizing and movement can at points assist the experience, but they can also hinder the release when it takes me out of the flow. Here my sensitivity to what takes me furthest is invaluable. The guidance of a rebirther can help me develop this sensitivity.

Another common method of disrupting my flow is called "checking out." This is a form of going to sleep which is not really sleep, but renders me unaware of my surroundings and radically slows my breathing. I can feel helpless in the face of it. Through my breathing I bring myself to a place where I will have to experience and release a significant fear if I am to proceed any further. When I check out, I decide to evacuate my body rather than feel it. When I do face the fear, however, suddenly I am no longer sleepy, but filled with feeling that I formerly believed I could not handle. Successfully breaking through this wall is accompanied by a significant increase in feeling alive.

I personally ran into such a wall for months in the course of rebirthing. Every time I set out to breathe fully, I got very sleepy and soon was busily dreaming despite every attempt of various rebirthers to keep me present. It was not until I brought myself to a place of safety, that I was willing to experience the degree of anger and fear that I had kept repressed. This place of safety was not only a degree of inner courage but also a safe outer environment, including a rebirther with whom I felt the comfort to experience that degree of anger.

Some rebirthers attribute this "checking out" to the degree of anesthetic experienced by the infant in the birth process. Anesthetic administered to the mother is transferred to the child through the mother's blood stream via the placenta. This produces such a degree of drowsiness and listlessness in some babies that they have to be vigorously revived after birth. The child's first experience of life outside the womb is in a drugged state. Using drugs to handle stress can be an addiction started at birth. The desire to "check out" of intense life situations whether using drugs or not can become a habit from day one.

The first rebirthers in Milwaukee did their sessions at my house. I came home one day to find a strange odor pervading the house. Hours earlier a woman had been rebirthed in my attic room. During her session at which three people were present, she and two of the observers all checked out. The rebirther also had a very difficult time staying alert as a distracting odor filled the room. Later the rebirthee recounted that at her actual birth someone dropped and broke a bottle of chloroform, making everyone in her delivery room very drowsy.

The most simple way to deal with the drowsiness you may begin to feel as you get close to a barrier is to be aware of it and consciously intend to stay alert. This works most of the time. If this does not handle it and the drowsiness continues or deepens, other waking up procedures may be employed. As a rebirther, I can usually sense the checking out process begin to happen before the rebirthee mentally leaves. This is accompanied by a psychic withdrawal and a diminishing of the breathing rhythm. At this point I psychically reaffirm their intention to stay present. I may also ask rebirthees to verbalize what they are feeling in their body. This helps them make a connection between what they are experiencing and their tendency to fade, giving more conscious choice in the process. I may sense a feeling being repressed and ask them to verbalize that emotion or express it to a significant person in their life. I may further ask rebirthees to alter their breathing rhythm or make a movement that increases and makes more congruent their energy flow. I may simply give feedback on what I see happening or even make a lighthearted comment. Trusting my observations and intuition, all of this is directed toward assisting the rebirthees who are in the process of releasing old holding patterns and granting themselves new positions of aliveness. Some rebirthees may need to go through this leaving and reentering process once or several times to discover their safety. I have the sense that some are going to another level of awareness in which the learning they need is more readily accepted. A few are even aware of what happens on other levels. The rebirther can be a helpful assistant in the process of waking up and feeling alive. Rebirthing is dissolving resistance to aliveness. In the end there is no substitute for simply continuing to breathe with the loving intention to increase your aliveness. This is sufficient unto itself. Waiting for a rebirther to come up with an answer or a clever technique for you is just another form of resistance.

In general, I try to assist most rebirthees in learning how to stay present emotionally, mentally and psychically throughout. Once I know organically that I do not have to leave my body (e.g., go to higher planes, die, ascend to heaven...) to be enlightened and fully alive, then I may more consciously choose to experiment with mastery of altered states. Before then, my flight from the physical may be continually reinforcing my fear of it.

FINDING YOUR PERSONAL LAW

The challenge of facing my barriers and waking up to my aliveness is the same in rebirthing as it is in life. In rebirthing we are intensifying the process, putting it under a magnifying glass for observation and healing. This takes us to the core of our resistance to life which may go unnoticed in everyday living. I listen very carefully for the core belief which underlies the resistance. This may appear spontaneously to the rebirthee. An affirmation of greater truth in the face of this limiting belief may be dealt with, almost unnoticed, by a simple affirmative breath. For example, it may occur to the rebirthee at some point that he or she is not worthy of feeling so good. Without hesitation the rebirthee may simply change this thought to "of course I am!" and take the next breath hardly even noting that this happened. On the other hand, in another session the rebirthee may have been struggling to "try to feel good" and become exhausted in the effort. At a point of despair the rebirthee may utter, "I can't do it." The basic attitude behind these words is the very thought against which the rebirthee has been pushing in an effort to feel good. Most often a recognition that this basic belief or personal law is what was behind the struggle brings great relief. I often simply and affirmatively point out "that is the thought behind your struggle," and then the person takes the first easy, releasing breath and starts to feel better. In our essence we all know that we are the creators of our life attitudes. Acceptance of this power in our core is the primary step in forgiveness, release and change.

Mary's discovery and owning of her choice to live dissolves her old personal law of not being responsible for her life.

MARY, AGE 36
THERAPIST

Breathing, I have the sensation of bright lights hurting my eyes, an ache on the side of my head. I feel a sharp pain of being separated from my mother – she is so far away in another room. I'm mad and I want my mama. I continue breathing. The pains pass. I have a clear memory of thinking, "this is not fun, I don't like it here, maybe I'll just leave." Then I have a strong sensation of being pulled toward my father and my sister who I imagine standing together looking at me. I feel that they definitely want me to live. I feel strong Love from them both. I think, "they want me to live..." I continue breathing. I think, "oh, what the heck, I made it this far, I might as well stay."

(I was delivered with forceps, got sick soon after my birth, lost weight, needed to be in an incubator. At one point my family was not sure if I would live.)

This session made it clear to me that I had a choice to live or not. The unconditional love I felt from my family was/is clear to me. I decided to live and grow at this time, in this space, with these parents and this sister. My choice, my decision, my responsibility was clear to me.

I know that I have had many issues and concerns resolved or let go of through breathing connectedly. My attitude toward myself, my self confidence, my vocation, my personal relations, even my financial affairs have changed significantly for the better since I began this process.

After one session, I sat up, looked out the window, observed afternoon sunlight, trees, street lined with cars, nothing unusual. I had an intense, keen sensation that, "everything is perfect exactly the way it is."

It is that spiritual sense of oneness, wholeness, perfection, that rebirthing reminds me of and that I can now remind myself of at any time.

PRACTICE FEELING GOOD

At the point where the breathing becomes easier, the rebirthees have opened the door to the pleasure and creativity inherent in being one with our source. It is important to practice and play with this kind of energy in order to become more familiar with it and make it a habit. Some rebirthees are ready to jump up and run off. This ending portion of the session is just as significant as all the rest. In fact, it is what it is all about – staying easily and pleasurably in my flow.

Significant releases in mental, emotional, and psychic blocking are always reflected in the body. The rebirthee's breathing looks and feels easier. Rather than just breathing in the chest or in the belly, at this point the whole body is usually inhaling and exhaling in union. My instruction is to continue staying in this flow "imagining" that the entire body is surrounded by an aura of light, healing energy, and that each breath takes nurturance into every cell of the body. In this medium, releasing insightful and creative activity abounds. The rebirthee often reports the feeling of "being breathed" rather than having to do anything. Some identify with the breath itself more than with the mechanism they used to think brought it about. This is the time during which we transform our cells to our light body.

It is during this time when I often write affirmations which seem appropriate for this birth into new life. Affirmations which assist the integration of a more positive personal law are particularly helpful. I ask rebirthees at the very end of our session to read these affirmations aloud, and like seeds in newly tilled soil, let them be planted in the place which feels best for them. I feel privileged to participate in the joy and light that rebirthees emit in the release of old limiting forms and the embracing of their essential life energy. The connection shared at this point is a treasure for both parties.

ACCEPTANCE OF YOUR PROCESS

Not every rebirthing leaves the rebirthee with a sense of total completion. Rebirthing is an opportunity to view and experience our patterns of physical, mental, emotional, and spiritual energies. I will only take in as much of this experience as I am ready to accept. Each time I open myself to the rebirthing process I push back the boundaries of fear and limitation. I build a bigger base of safety. I do not lose what I have gained. I may ignore it for a while. I have that privilege. But the next time I am willing to surrender fully, I go on to take the next step in my process. Acceptance of how I am holding back, where my limits are and the fears I have yet to release, is critical part of my total acceptance. If I fight this and put criticism and pressure on myself to be somewhere else, I will feel uncomfortable. Both the rebirthing process and the rebirther are there to assist me in the acceptance of where I am right now. It is I who must conclude that being me at this point in my process is OK. Once this valve to my heart is open, my natural flow of aliveness does the rest and I feel wonderful. Some rebirthings are spectacular. Some are peaceful and serene. All show me where I am at in the moment. If I flee from the openness of my heart back to the judgment in my head, I can stop or cut off whatever flow I have generated and feel miserable. This is also part of my divine privilege and an important lesson many of us must discover. But I am the boss. There are no lousy rebirthings; there are only lousy conclusions I can reach about them.

My rebirthing may have opened a path for me to follow. This path may be scary, sad or laden with frustrations. It may take faith in my inner healing process to follow it, not seeing the endpoint. I may have misgivings and concerns. With trust in my inner guidance, however, finally getting on the path and out of the trap is always a relief.

INTEGRATING YOUR REBIRTHING INTO LIFE

Most rebirthees are feeling quite open and relaxed after the process. I suggest to the rebirthee to consciously continue to breathe easily and freely for at least the next hour. I encourage them to take care of themselves as they would a newborn, rather than close down emotionally as soon as they walk out the door. This helps to integrate this clear feeling into their lives, rather than keep it associated with just the rebirthing room. After all, it is in my daily life where it counts most to maintain and apply the new attitudes and conclusions I have reached about myself. I usually suggest a period of at least a week in–between sessions to allow the attitudes to settle in and for practice in using them to take place. During this time it is helpful to read the rebirthing affirmations at least once a day to reinforce my changes. Like moving into a new living space, taking up residence in my light body may take some getting used to.

Challenges in the form of old stimuli to which I have formerly reacted negatively will arise in the course of living. Here is where I believe the greatest value of the rebirthing process emerges. Since I have trained myself in the session to breathe in a deep and releasing way in the face of every challenge, a deep and clearing breath taken in the midst of a life challenge signals me to remember my safety and to trust my inner resources. This split second of recentering signaled by my breath is often exactly what it takes for me to support myself rather than to sell out to negative reactions. Even if I think I have already sold out, a deep and clearing breath can bring me back to my truth and inner forgiveness which allows me to learn what I need from the situation and to proceed lovingly with self care. It makes no difference what has happened, what only counts is the conclusion I have reached about it. My conclusion either increases aliveness and acceptance or reinforces fear and resistance. That power is always in my hands. The rebirthing breath is my constant reminder of this power. It is only I who can take my next breath and create my world with it.

Part of the responsibility of knowing that this power is within me is being intelligent about how to nurture and foster its growth. This means being honest enough about myself and how I operate to choose the people and settings to support my chosen path. As a rebirther I recommend readings in spiritual growth, the use of affirmations, seminars and groups which promote self–exploration, a daily practice in breath awareness and continuing the rebirthing process itself, first with a rebirther and eventually with peers who are confident with their process.

The desire to discount my progress and stop my process may arise in equal proportion to the fear of the divine power I am approaching. Indeed my ego will fear its death. I prefer to see the ego as being transformed, just as my body is, into a vehicle fitting my divine expression. This is death in the sense that I will not be the same as I was, I will change form. It is also birth, however, in the sense of an entry into a more free and creative existence.

This fear of death, limiting beliefs, emotional and physical discomfort which occasionally arises in the rebirthing session can also rear up in–between sessions. Here is where it becomes patently evident that it was not some magic performed by the rebirther (doctor substitute) which saved my life. The same process of breathing with faith in my inner healing life force works outside the session as well as during a rebirthing session. I just focus on my healing intention, activate my breathing, surrender to my experience, release what is negative and affirm what enhances my aliveness. Having done this in session teaches my body the method. I learn to adjust my breath, my attitude, my thoughts and even my body posture to facilitate release. This becomes a lifelong habit. I adjust my breathing as well as the depth of the process I engender to the circumstances. If I am at home and have the time and space I might lie down on my bed and do a full connected breathing cycle for an hour or even longer. If I am on the bus or at Thanksgiving dinner, I might simply take a few deep affirming breaths and work with my thoughts. I soon learn to attend to my breathing in every situation. I do not reserve the releasing breath and affirmative thinking for the consultation room.

As I advance in the skill with the daily application of rebirthing, I learn to listen with increasingly greater sensitivity to the messages from my body, its subtle flows of energy. I learn to hear the balance of harmony in my inner dialogue. I keep myself for longer and longer periods in the center of my divine light. I become practiced in breathing into or with physical sensations as a process of self–care. I grow to accept my experiences rather than resist or avoid them. This is what is meant by flowing with life. It is my breath which initiates and directs this flow.

Through daily application I am taught by the spirit of breath. I learn that breath is the spirit which generates the thoughts which manifest my body. On the physical level breath is the process of bringing air in and out of my lungs and being nurtured by as well as nurturing my environment. On the mental level, breathing is the dynamic that gives life to new ideas and brings harmony to old ones. On the spiritual level, breathing is the movement of my creative spirit, the force that generates life. Spiritually, rebirthing is attunement to the spirit of breath. This is the secret of the masters.

KNOWING WHEN A SESSION IS OVER

A rebirthing session generally includes a full breathing cycle. That is a build–up of energy, a release of resistance and an acceptance of a greater level of peace and flow. A session can comprise several cycles or only a partial cycle depending on the needs and openness of the individuals involved. Part of spiritual wisdom is knowing when you have reached a plateau and how to let yourself integrate your progress, rather than trying to climb the whole mountain at once and falling to the bottom each time. Mostly, there is an inner sense of completion when your cycle is complete. Feedback from your rebirther can help develop this sense.

HOW MANY REBIRTHINGS TO DO

The number of rebirthing sessions to undertake will vary depending upon your goals and your ease in reaching them. One session can open the floodgates for massive change or just give you a taste of your potential. Five to ten sessions with a rebirther are recommended for learning the process well enough to feel confident in rebirthing yourself. Some need more, some less.

My style is to combine counseling with rebirthing which allows one mode to assist the other in the uncovering and releasing process. I often intersperse breathing with verbal sessions when doing a series. I do this not by a prearranged formula but according to the individual's needs and wants at the time of the session.

If an individual's goals are to address specific issues which rebirthing can aid, these needs may be met in one or a few sessions. If the goals are more far–reaching, the number of sessions may be more.

Again, spiritual wisdom dictates knowing when to take a break from formal sessions. Our growth continues always, and sometimes we do not recognize this or acknowledge that our goals are met until we step back and see it. Discerning between taking a break and running away at a critical point is a matter ultimately for inner guidance. The experience and feedback of your rebirther is also of great assistance. Trusting and supporting deeper levels of yourself, however, is what rebirthing is about.

COMPLETION IN REBIRTHING

Completion in rebirthing is both a state of being and an endpoint in a process. From the perspective of the Yin, being side of me, completion in rebirthing is experiencing and accepting my spiritual perfection. I will never be more of a divine spirit than I am now, no matter what I accomplish in my life. I am complete as I live in the state of divine acceptance. This does not mean that I always look, think or feel blissful. It means that regardless of my temporary doubts or feelings, an underlying self–acceptance is intact. I may even try to convince myself that I have given up or sold out, but the connection to my deeper being cannot be destroyed. This is true whether I recognize it or not with my conscious mind. Completion is the state of experiencing that I am more than my conscious mind. As this experience grows so does the awareness and sense of completion.

From the Yang, doing and having side of me, completion in rebirthing means reaching goals in major areas of my life, or mastering the "Five Biggies":

BIRTH DRAMA

Is the enactment of the major limiting theme or personal law my mind has incorporated in my body to be dealt with in this life. For example, a theme such as "I must struggle to survive" may be acted out in an arduous labor. A belief that "I hurt the women I love" may be portrayed in perineal tearing during birth. Completion involves getting to these core negative beliefs, exposing the lie that I am helpless and reversing the pattern in a way that is life–affirming.

PARENTAL DISAPPROVAL SYNDROME

Is the system of limiting beliefs I have accepted in relationship with my parents or parent substitutes. This involves some form of seeing my safety and happiness dependent upon them and directing my life energy toward approval seeking or rebellion. Thus, I must get their approval or show them that they are wrong to be OK with myself. Completion is reowning my inner source of safety and fulfillment, loving myself in the face of anyone else's opinions without having to be defensive or closed to do it.

SPECIFIC NEGATIVES

Are the collection of negative beliefs taken on by my ego usually through decisions made in contact with important life influences other than my parents, e.g. teachers, relatives, friends, etc. I generally assume those limiting beliefs which support my personal law and parental disapproval syndrome. Completion involves unlocking and releasing the specific patterns of belief and repressed feelings that reinforce my denial regardless of their source.

UNCONSCIOUS DEATH URGE

Is the mistaken belief that one must destroy the body to gain freedom. This is akin to destroying the movie screen because we do not like the movie. When I deny my divine source I seem to place my life at the mercy of outside forces – a vengeful God, the devil, illness – all of which weaken and eventually destroy my body. Completion is reowning my connection to eternal life such that any changes of physical form are conscious and harmonious.

MULTILEVEL KARMA

Is the retaining of negative cause and effect relationships from other levels of our existence and applying them to our present conscious life. Regardless of how attractive our past beliefs are or where this "past" came from, our power to change is only in the present. Completion here is forgiving and releasing all past or future negative relationships. I do not have to make up for anything to anyone nor does anyone have to make up to me. We are divine equals.

Obviously completion of these Five Biggies is completion in life. Completion is not the end or termination. Completion is a putting in order in the present which allows for a new beginning, a starting point of clarity, truth and balance. Completion allows me to play fully and creatively in my world. It generates true enthusiasm and joy in the life process. As I start out from a sense of completion, I face each life event without dread from the past or anticipation for the future. To the external observer I may seem to be leading the same life, but from my vantage point, each step has lost its weightiness and the illusion of drama has been lifted. I see the interplay of light beings with a safety and peace that I did not have to destroy my body to try to achieve.

On the physical level, Yin completion means awareness of living in my light body; Yang completion means mastering the ability to heal parts of my body in releasing the breath energy within them. On the mental level, Yin completion means accepting the clarity of being beyond my mind, not trapped in it; Yang completion means the ability to resolve conflicting mental messages and generate a higher thought. On the spiritual level, Yin completion is accepting my present enlightenment; Yang completion is mastery of the breath by breath growth in awareness and manifestation of my divinity in every aspect of my existence.

Rebirthing heightens awareness and aliveness. Any imbalances stand out. Rebirthing helps bring up the energy to address these imbalances. It is I, with or without the assistance of a rebirther, who must have the courage to apply this reawakened energy in healing ways to restore balance. It is my loving intention to do this which is the healing, not the rebirthing. It is also I who experience and acknowledge the restoration of my centeredness, or at least know enough of what I must do on my own to get there. At this point, I may naturally discontinue formal sessions with a rebirther. This, however, can be just the beginning of another phase of rebirthing.

SELF–REBIRTHING

Rebirthing does not stop when I no longer do formal sessions. Another level of its power now emerges for those who do not shut down here. The process, the spirit of breath, will continue to teach and guide me as long as I have the courage to listen. I will develop increasing sensitivity to my inner guidance using my breath in at least two ways. First, I will set aside times to focus on the rebirthing breath on my own or with others equally confident with their rebirthing. I will do this either regularly or as needed or both. Second, I will discover that I am, in a broader sense, rebirthing all the time. The building up and letting down of energy cycles is happening continuously in my life and my breath is assisting me through it all. I will become increasingly sensitive to the nuances of my breathing process on a moment by moment basis.

This will magnify and amplify the power and options I have to exercise in each situation. I will develop creative ways to rebirth that look nothing like the formal sessions with which I started. For example, I have learned to focus on my creative breath when I am walking my dog, jogging and bathing, using a different breath in each circumstance. Starting my day with connected breathing in the bathtub has brought me not only more energy, but also creative ideas that have allowed me to do more with less effort. Each person adapts his or her rebirthing to life in the ways suited to him or her.

David creatively expanded upon the discoveries he made with his rebirther to give himself and his son a gift of new aliveness.

DAVID, AGE 44
HEART SURGEON

For me, the experience of the rebirthing phenomenon has taken the shape of an internal journey, a felt body experience which then expands outward into light and joy. Twice this has surfaced fully, the first being my first rebirthing experience with you, Jim, and the second being an experience several months later, alone, early one morning in bed shortly after being awakened by the sun. Sensing a pregnant moment in time, I decided to combine the connected breathing technique with a Yoga technique called the 61 point meditation or a journey of awareness through the body starting at the forehead and moving through 61 steps through the entire body. In this situation, I used the breath to enliven each area and then moved on to the next. After progressing through the head and neck, upper extremities, chest and abdomen, I became aware of a need to shift the pattern slightly to travel the right leg before the left. At one point, it was as if some critical mass was reached and I suddenly experienced my entire body, including the areas not yet covered, exploding into light and energy, as if each cell became a tiny star of creation. The experience was very similar to the one shared with you several months previously and I was at once appreciative of that original gift and of my ability to see my own light. My entire life came together at one point in time, seeing several antecedent currents leading to that point and a couple ways that the current must travel from that point. Several areas of my body experienced release of tensions and my entire being became full, overflowing, first into tears of appreciation, and then into laughter of the kind I had not remembered. Deeper and deeper it rumbled until it awakened my son sleeping in his room above me. Coming to see what was going on, he could not understand but did know that it was good, and curled up beside me to share in the light that he felt. As the physical and emotional elements gradually moved into a new balance, I experienced an internal sense of aliveness which I took with me into my "new" day. Again, feeling newly created, newly born, I marveled at the beauty that we carry within us and felt deeply appreciative of all the events that had led up to that moment in time.

Advanced rebirthing is advanced self–trust and safety. It is not highly esoteric or complicated. The path is open for each of us and we do not have to learn computer language or travel to a foreign country to find it. Once I have given myself permission to sit fully in the driver's seat of my life there is no greater thrill, nothing more interesting or entertaining. The ride is fantastic – don't hold your breath.

REBIRTHING AND PHYSICAL IMMORTALITY

The natural conclusion to gaining mastery with our breath is that of harmony in body, mind and spirit. This means that our body perfectly reflects the instructions of our spirit and that we are mentally conscious of what instructions we are giving. Rebirthing is the process of creating harmony and increasing consciousness.

Body mastery is not a goal reserved for a few yogis living in caves or for saints with special powers removed from the earthly domain. It is the direct and immediate goal of each one of us who has a body on this planet. Mastery is the ability to use our body directly, effectively and pleasurably in achieving our purpose on earth. Unless we open our awareness to how we are already accomplishing this goal, we will hold ourselves back in ignorance and fear. Our bodies are miracles of life and will continue to be until we give it or accept the instructions to die, that is, radically change our forms. It is only us who can give these instructions to our bodies. We are in the process of becoming more conscious of how we do this as well as of how we can do something different. With each breath I take I put energy into whatever my beliefs are. If I cling to beliefs of illness, aging and death as inevitable, then this is what I create.

Metaphysically, birth and death are not a tragedy because nothing spiritually is ever lost. The tragedy psychologically is that we deny that we are responsible for these changes. We then blame outside forces and try to convince others of our helplessness. I am not claiming to be conscious of every instruction I am giving to my body. I am certainly blinding myself from the truth, however, if I refuse to look at the results. I compound the lie if I assign responsibility for my body to the doctor, germs or some idea of God that is not part of my higher self. In so doing, I play victim and perpetuate the original sin – denial of my divine source. Physical immortality is taking 100% responsibility for my aliveness now. It is not pretending to know everything consciously now, but it is certainly not pretending to be ignorant in my higher self. It is affirming the wisdom of my higher self, coming into harmony with it, and dedicating each moment of my existence to a more fully conscious embracing of my total being.

When I say that I am physically immortal, I am telling my highest truth. This leads to greater awareness and mastery. It affirms my essential being. When I say that I and everyone must die, I am telling the truth of a limited version of being. This "limited truth" also produces results in accordance with its commands, that is, more illusion of limited reality in which I and others are victimized and helpless.

Physical immortality does not mean clinging on to my present physical form as long as possible because I am afraid of change. This is no better than killing myself because I am afraid of being here. Our goal is not seeing who can hang on to their body the longest, but rather how we can increase our divine awareness of every change we make. As a physical immortalist I am dedicated to releasing fear of every aspect of my existence. I may choose to change physical form in a way that looks like disease and involuntary death to others and perhaps even to parts of myself. My highest vision and faith, however, is always to embrace responsibility for any choices which increase my awareness and mastery. The key word in the accepting of responsibility is ***now***. Even as you read this your heart is opening or closing to the call to aliveness. You are in charge of this process. Your mind may bring up every objection to the concept of responsibility for total aliveness. This can be your excuse to close down. See if you are willing to listen to the simple child–like impulse beyond your mental objections that knows that you always were and will always be a presence in the "here and now" that is not bound by the particular forms around you. It is only in this now that you embrace total aliveness. Every time I make this choice, I reduce the energy that I have committed to my limited, negative version of reality. I take the life forms around me less heavily. I see the light and truth in all more and more. I literally transform my vision of the world. I save the world from my old disparaging view of it and help create the atmosphere in which others are invited to embrace their eternal light and life.

I will always have a form and a body as long as I am a divine being – not necessarily a physical form or body. Death does not eliminate my body, it is a change of form. Both birth and death are illusions insofar as they look like something is ultimately lost or gained. As a spirit I take on particular forms to accomplish my purpose. Life is not better or worse after I die. My purpose is the same and so are my challenges as an evolving being. The forms may change but the essence remains. The realization of this may at first be shocking.

There is no place to go that is better or allows me to hide from my growth. Here and now is all there is. It is in the present that I can remove the layers of limited illusion to unveil the Garden of Eden in which I am already sitting, and greet the divine companions that are waiting for me to acknowledge them. After the initial shock of this truth diminishes I can breathe easy because I know that there is no place to go other than here and now. What remains is simply the process of increasing my mastery and enjoyment of my divine self – to increasingly incorporate my transformations. This is the state of physical immortality. Rebirthing is what I do in this state.

Steeped in a life of religious tradition, Evelyn found the breath adding a profound experiential dimension to a sacred spiritual symbol for her.

EVELYN, AGE 56
MOTHER

My most significant rebirth experience was recently when during complete relaxation – I became clearly aware of energy flowing in my body, first in an up–down sensation, then side to side, presenting to me the subtle powerful image of a cross.

It was a beautiful change from the usual perspective of the symbolism of the cross.

HOW TO REBIRTH YOURSELF – THE FINAL WORD

Using trained rebirthers and spiritual guides can be very wise. If they are wise they know that they are no doing it for me, but rather assisting me to learn how to rebirth myself. Ultimately, it is only I who can open the gate to the Garden of Eden, that state of responsible consciousness, by reaccepting my divine source. This is the state of physical immortality.

Some beliefs would say this is heresy because only God can save me. Of course it is only God that can save me – the God I must embrace within me. Our greatest fear is not the terrible things we may find if we look inside. These may seem scary but they are minor compared to the fear of accepting the power of our divine source within. To discover this source destroys the limited self–image of my ego. I must then be 100% responsible for myself and my world. I can no longer conveniently hide. I must listen to and follow this inner guidance directly. I must face my ego's fear of death to do this and that is why there is so much resistance to it. Rebirthing myself means consciously facing this fear of death and bringing myself safely into life beyond death. Other beliefs would say that it is blasphemy to affirm that I am God. Of course it is blasphemy to think my limited ego version of "I" (the sinner, the one who denies God) is God. It is precisely this form of pride which must be released to embrace the greater "I" that is one with the divine source. Continually affirming limitation, however, does not provide the key to this release. Rebirthing myself is exercising faith in the inner source through every physical sensation, emotional feeling or mental doubt I can have. Herein lies the transformative power of self–rebirthing.

CHAPTER FIVE

BEING A REBIRTHER

Assisting others in the process of breathing fully and freely while affirming their safety in body, mind and spirit is the goal of the rebirther or breath guide. This is symbolically the oldest profession, initiated by God in the creation of Adam. God taught Adam to put life into his mud. Today the atoms are already assembled and walking around. The rebirther's job is to be an effective coach in the continuing process of self–transformation. In one sense we are all called to be a rebirther inasmuch as we participate in the divine creative act of being alive. Either by example or by profession we are all rebirthers.

THE REBIRTHER'S ROLE

The rebirther's role from an active "Yang" perspective is to be a teacher giving feedback and suggestions to the rebirthee in the process of release. With experience a rebirther can read the holding patterns in mind and body simply by observing the breathing of a rebirthee. The instructions given to the rebirthee may be on many levels from the verbal to the psychic. The rebirther may at times be using knowledge or intuition, but the goal is single pointed.

All techniques are secondary in importance to the healing presence the rebirther provides. It is this presence which helps create the medium of acceptance and safety in which the rebirthee is invited to release fear. If I, as a rebirther, am not affirming my own safety and trust in the face of my doubts and fears, how can I expect my rebirthees to affirm safety and trust in their process. I am not suggesting that as a rebirther I must be free of all fear and doubts to be effective. As a rebirther, I must have faith in the healing presence I provide beyond any misgivings or emotional turmoil I may encounter in rendering my service. Further, and even more important, I must have faith in the natural healing spirit of the rebirthee. One of the greatest skills I can develop as a rebirther is to get out of the way and allow the rebirthee's inner healing process to happen. My inner guidance as a rebirther has very often congratulated me on a wonderful insight or suggestion I have shared with a rebirthee, and then instructed me to keep my mouth shut and step aside to let the rebirthee's higher self lead the way.

As a rebirther, I am a model of translating what seems to be "attack" thoughts, i.e., limiting or negative opinions about myself and my world, into instantaneous release. This release always uncovers the loving intention behind the defensive or attacking posture. A rebirthee, for example, may angrily demand to know what my credentials are to be a rebirther. If I respond to that person only as an attacking individual and am afraid for my self–image, I am reinforcing both of our fears of being hurt. If I see that rebirthees are often fearful of being hurt and the ultimate intention behind their communication is to take care of themselves, I can respond in a way that reinforces the self–caring intention while reducing the fear. Fear reinforces fear; safety reinforces safety. I, as a rebirther, can help my rebirthees see through their fears to their basic self–caring impulses in all of their life situations. I may start out with some verbal translation of their behavior into terms which highlight their self–caring intentions. I will go further to assist them to connect free and easy breathing with the process of seeing through fear and feeling the freedom this brings in their bodies. Eventually, the very act of breathing becomes more associated with release and freedom than with fear and attack. This is life transformation.

As a rebirther, I model this process of translating attack into release by getting benefit out of each form of feedback from the rebirthee. If I resist praise or confrontation, exhilaration or withdrawal, the intellectual or the emotional, I demonstrate blockage of energy flow. My challenge as a rebirther is to discover in each form of feedback the healing intention behind it and to assist the rebirthee to direct this energy into channels which increase aliveness, self–acceptance and pleasurable, harmonious breathing.

REBIRTHEES AS MY TEACHER

Whenever I as a rebirther am ready for my next lesson and therefore ready to go to my next level of service to others, my rebirthees are there to teach it to me. They always require me to let go of my ready–made answers, formulas or instructions. They present me with the opportunity to listen more closely and reach out more effectively. This means releasing attachment to my old rules and perhaps even breaking them to achieve a higher result. As a therapist/rebirther, for example, I am regularly called to discriminate between what is actually helping a client to help themselves and what is enabling them to depend on me or others outside of themselves for their strength. This translates into very practical concerns such as how much contact do I have with a rebirthee in between sessions, what if they feel in crisis, can they call me?

A recent rebirth client with a very traumatic background of incest and physical abuse began to uncover very powerful memories and feelings during our sessions. This in turn led to more "flashbacks" and a profound sense of helplessness at times in between rebirths. She consciously took responsibility for these feelings and attempted to use self–help skills, but still wanted occasional reassurance and support when she felt her process getting overwhelming. I responded to her phone calls which became more frequent the deeper she went. This required on my part a moment by moment assessment of what would be most genuinely supportive of her growth. As long as I could feel good about her integrating and applying my emotional and mental feedback, I had an inner "green light" to extend myself further than I had before and be balanced. When, however, her calls lapsed into repeated advice seeking, casual conversation and the kind of support that is more appropriate to a reciprocal friendship, I felt uncomfortable and had to set a limit to our contact. Although this seemed initially rejecting to her, it allowed her to develop other life recourses both internal and eternal and she was grateful for this direction. I learned from her about extending myself, deepening my work, and still staying aware and taking care of myself in the process.

I often get clients who have been in many forms of therapy and/or growth work over extended periods. I do not prejudge and assume that this was bad for them or that they were wasting their time. In fact, I assume that they were doing whatever they needed to in order to get them this far. I also assume that they will continue to their next stage of growth when we are complete with our work together. Some years back, I was referred a client who was labeled as resistant to change. She did rebirthing with me and graduated from our School of Spiritual Psychology.

She assisted in the programs and gave of herself readily yet she still tended to freeze and hold back after years. I did not sense a "game playing" attitude of resistance yet I was often baffled as to how to proceed. She caused me to listen more carefully and intuitively than ever before. I had to let go of every technique I had ever learned and be with her until I heard. Finally a whole new picture began to emerge. Beneath the confident, assertive, successful woman who had accomplished many of her life goals, was a terrified little girl who recoiled from the slightest hint of intimacy and the manipulation she expected to follow. Even being asked "How are you?" by someone she liked, especially a man, would produce an unconscious defensiveness. Being heard and then bringing this to the surface was very difficult for her, but also a tremendous relief. The door opened to reuniting with her lost little girl and intimacy became an actuality versus a potential.

My rebirthees expand my consciousness and help me develop new techniques every week. They take me into undreamed of realms. Each rebirthee has created a unique universe from his or her application of divine creative ability. Our universes overlap, but are never the same. As I acknowledge the validity of their reality, I do not discount mine. This produces awakening for both of us. What I learn from one rebirthee helps me with another. In rebirthing clients who have physical handicaps, for example, I have been exposed to both the pain and the power of being physically challenged. I am impressed with the many levels of healing that take place when going through medical procedures like surgery and the diversity of choices we make in use of our bodies for the purpose of healing and teaching in this lifetime. Rebirthing has brought me together with my closest colleagues, friends, and creative companions on this spiritual journey whom I would never have found had I stayed in the seclusion of my own world.

CONTACT

My effectiveness as a breath guide is increased on the Yin side by my own clarity and freedom in body, mind and spirit. On the Yang side my effectiveness is increased by my ability to make essential contact and clear contracts with my rebirthees.

Contact with my rebirthee begins on the psychic level before we ever meet physically. How rebirther and rebirthee attract each other is influenced by who they are willing to let into their lives and for what purposes. My general intention is to connect with rebirthees on an essential level. This means my divine core with their divine core. Even though we use our personalities as the telephone apparatus, it is our essence which does the real communication. If I limit my contact to two egos trying to impress one another or to share comforting jargon, this sets the tone for the level of work we will do together. This does not mean I always ask soul–searching questions or respond with my deepest feelings. It does mean that I am responsible for the quality of my contact as a rebirther, before, during and after my sessions.

Rebirthees will bring to a rebirthing session exactly what they bring to life. They will tend to recreate with me, the rebirther, the forms of contact they have with important others in their life. They may initiate as many styles of interaction as our fertile imaginations have created on this planet. If any one style causes me, as a rebirther, to lose contact with my own essence, to get trapped in my own personality patterns, then I help reinforce belief in their being trapped within their patterns. It then is two egos selling each other their forms of limitation. My job, as a rebirther, is to stay in contact with my own essence, even when my personality is engaged with the rebirthees. This helps create the precedent for the rebirthee to do the same. Then the personality interactions can be instructive. I, as a rebirther, can share how my personality responds to the rebirthees, and have it be loving and beneficial because I am approaching balance and truth about my own personality. This fosters a contact bathed in love and openness because it is directed by my essence. The content of our interaction may even look like old personality routines, but the quality of our contact will help see through and release the hold that these old patterns have had over our behavior.

I rebirthed a fellow psychologist who was very intelligent and well trained in traditional verbal therapy and appreciative of transference issues. She made a comment on our initial meeting about my reputation for being a "salesman of some renown." Coming from someone else this remark would probably have had little impact, but I was aware of my own personality's desire to make a good impression. Though I did not become visibly defensive, I was internally aware of my defensive reaction. I was simultaneously aware that this person was here to do important work for herself not to be impressed by me. Rather than interpret or highlight this remark, I chose to focus on our intent in rebirthing and then later, as our rapport grew, to share more of my internal process. I knew I was working on both the essential and the personality level and that both were part of the healing in process. She responded and became much more open and available to her heart, changing both her career and her personal life to what was more fulfilling to her. She did not need to put others at a distance in her initial encounters and was less fearful of being sold what was not beneficial to her true self.

When the quality of my contact with another is not feeling good and I feel stuck, it is because I have slipped out of contact with my own essence. Once I have reowned my essential power, I can take the necessary steps to improving my contact with the other. This may involve sharing something I have been holding back, changing my perception of the other, releasing my fears and/or giving each other more space and trust. Determining the quality of contact within myself and with another is primary in any interaction. The rebirther/rebirthee relationship is an opportunity to practice creating the highest quality of contact we can, because it is dedicated to and practices the spirit of breath mastery and essential harmony. This relationship is the model for the depth of how we can relate to one another and serve each other's highest good.

CONTRACT

That both rebirther and rebirthee are successful in obtaining the results they seek is influenced by the agreements with which they start out. As a rebirther, it is my responsibility to set up an effective contract. This means being clear with the rebirthee about our respective roles and goals. This further means that I operate with integrity in carrying them out. If I say that I am a breath guide but act like a savior, I am giving mixed messages and will get mixed results. For example, I may help reinforce the rebirthee in acting responsible, but feeling dependent. To make a clear contract with another, I must be clear on who I am and what I can do. I may use the role of rebirther to function as a consultant, teacher, guide, guru, therapist, friend, savior, etc. Each role has different expectations of the parties involved. My position as a rebirther is to take 100% responsibility to use my knowledge and intuition in giving feedback and encouragement while assisting the rebirthee to breathe fully and freely with self–acceptance. I see the rebirthee's role as taking 100% responsibility for using the technique to increase aliveness and mastery of life. Both parties are responsible for the conclusions they reach and the results they achieve. I assume that if there is a suggestion I make that the rebirthee does not feel is best, that he or she will exercise their right to do something different. My supporting of this right helps communicate that the highest allegiance is to personal growth, not to me and my opinions. My belief is that our connection is essential and for our mutual evolution, and that it does not always cater to our egos.

I was recently assisting a client in her process who was feeling trapped in her job. She had given heart and soul to it and although she loved her work was still feeling stifled in her relationship to it. I suggested externalizing this relationship and gave her a small, soft pillow to represent her heart. My intention was to have her separate from this symbolically and notice how it felt by putting the pillow in a chair that represented her job. I asked her to do this and she adamantly refused, clutching defiantly on to the pillow. I immediately saw the strength and self care in her response, ignoring my instructions and holding on to what was dear to her. I immediately cheered for her, without premeditation, seeing that she went directly to the goal without following my idea of how to get there. I surprised her and myself with my cheer, and we both instantaneously knew that she had moved off her old holding position of doing what she was supposed to at the sacrifice of what she loved.

Beyond our general contract, there are particular agreements as to time, place, length of session, cost and payment, etc. These will depend on whether you are rebirthing as a friend, associate or professional. The more integrity maintained in each of these agreements, the more energy is put into clear results and the model of integrity is breathed into your life. Depending on how I define my role as a rebirther and what I believe assists my effectiveness, I will request different information from the rebirthee as part of our rebirthing agreement. I may want to know about their original birth process, their family system, emotionally significant events in their past, their current relationship status, etc.

As a rebirther, I personally look for the rebirthee's major life themes and how they come to bear on their present life challenges. In so doing, we are working together in unlocking and releasing life programs that are limiting and no longer useful. Our contract calls for mutual participation in a discovery process rather than an expert telling someone less informed how to live. I teach the rebirthee to be more aware of emotional and physical energies and encourage communication about them. This both heightens awareness and increases safety in sharing.

Individuals often seek out the rebirthing process at times of major life transition – going from one state to another (consciously and sometimes physically). This is reminiscent of their first great change of state in a body – from intrauterine life to life outside the womb. Birth symbolizes what we go through in making our transition. The rebirthee recalls and to varying degrees recreates the limitations of these original transition patterns, e.g., being alone, feeling resistance or stuckness, panic, having the world tipped upside down, confusion, lack of support, etc. The rebirthee's agreement in the rebirthing process is to admit these attitudes into awareness, to continue breathing through them and to reach new conclusions about present life positions – physical, emotional, mental and spiritual. This allows the rebirthee to rewrite the script on life change.

My contact and contract with a rebirthee begins on a psychic level before the session and continues throughout as well as after our session. Continuing to support each other's highest good in thought and attitude is part of the rebirthing exchange. Having touched each other's essence in a conscious manner, returning to the illusions of our egos is a breach of contract. Especially when rebirthees are in the throes of major transformations emotionally and mentally, I may, as a rebirther, find myself aware of their drama even when we are not physically together. It is then that I say a prayer of support for their process.

Diane's sensitive support as a rebirther to her rebirthee, Betty Lou, shows how her connectedness before, during, and after their session is a positive ally in the Divine healing process.

DIANE, AGE 42
COURT CLERK

One of my most significant rebirth experiences with a client was one with an exceptionally lovely young woman named Betty Lou. Betty Lou is suffering from that life draining, devitalizing killer disease called leukemia. She was struggling with the decision to have a bone marrow transplant, suggested by the medical profession. She was fearing the traumatic side effects and was toying with the option of giving up and dying. Betty Lou has a lovely three year old child and devoted husband she would be leaving behind.

We had an appointment at 10 a.m. one morning for her first rebirth. I took my precious daughter, Danielle, to her sitter and waited patiently until 10:30 a.m.. Then I decided to call her to check if she still planned on coming. I woke her from a deep sleep. She had had a very uncomfortable night and said she felt awful and couldn't come. I gently suggested that our resistance to healing comes in many forms and said it was OK and we could do it some other time and hung up.

Not three minutes later my phone rang and it was Betty Lou saying this is the time she might need to do this most. She asked if it is was too late to still come and she came.

When she arrived I noted her devitalized condition. She was suffering extreme exhaustion. Her skin was a gray, lifeless color. Her eyelids were heavy and struggling to remain open. Her movements were slowed and her attitude was one of defeat, despair and hopelessness.

We talked long enough for me to establish some rapport, to obtain some information on her background, to define her beliefs on life and death, also to put her at greater ease with me and the process. I explained the technique we would be using and we proceeded upstairs to begin.

She laid down on my bed and got warm and comfortable. We began the breathing and after just a short time she said "My God, I can't believe this," and if she said it once, she said it ten times. Her whole being was vibrating with delight. She kept insisting she was vibrating off of the bed. I, too, could see the subtle movement. Consciously she experienced the Christ light moving within her. She became aware of the Power of God she contained within her being. Her realization that she possessed the free will to use this God given power to choose to live and go on was profound for her. She saw that, if there was this power within her, she could and would heal her disease. She realized she had the power; it wasn't outside of herself. The answer was within. The light was right there within her.

She stood up from that death–bed attitude absolutely vibrant. There was healthy color in her face. She had pink cheeks. Her eyes were brilliant and sparkling. Her attitude was positive and she had chosen to live. She saw her own Power. She was completely revitalized, bubbling with energy and excitement. That one single session did not heal her leukemia, but it helped her to see her options and realize her personal power to act on them. It let her experience the healing energy flowing through her body. It gave her a peek at the possibilities available through spiritual healing. Only God heals and she had just connected up with God and used God's power to move a level of consciousness. The breathing simply put her in a place where she could hear more and see more of who she really is. And that is God.

Today, Betty Lou is working with a Holistic clinic; treating her challenge with nutrition, vitamins and God. She was tickled that she should be mentioned in a book and play a part being recorded in history.

It is the rebirthees' job to trust their intuition in selecting a rebirther. It is the rebirther's job to assist them in so doing. This may be by suggesting another rebirther before initiating the process if the rebirther is not OK with the contact and contract, or if the rebirthee would be better served by another rebirther.

In most instances there is a synchronicity which brings the rebirther and rebirthee together. The rebirther has something to share which is perfect for the rebirthee's next level of growth. Also, the rebirthee presents the rebirther with exactly what the rebirther needs to grow. I like to think God is right outside my door sending in the next person who is perfect for my next lesson. A rebirther who thinks he or she has all the answers and nothing to learn is a contradiction. By definition, the rebirther is teaching a process of learning and growing breath by breath. The rebirther demonstrates this process while performing his or her greatest service.

It takes both self–esteem and humility for a rebirther to know that he or she is both a teacher and, at the same time, in the presence of a divine master in the form of a rebirthee. The rebirthee may not be aware of this, but it is the rebirther's task to help lead the rebirthee to the awareness of their master within.

In the rebirthing session itself, the rebirthee may bring forth a challenge that the rebirther is struggling to handle in his or her own psyche. There is no rule book on how to deal with this for the rebirther, except to follow the principles of truth, simplicity and love. The rebirther is there to share the best of what he or she has, not to act like he or she has it all together. The rebirther may or may not share openly what is going on internally. Nonetheless, the rebirther supports the self–esteem of both parties. To know that one has a healing energy to share, even when one's conscious mind is self–critical, is a challenge for anyone in a helping role. For rebirthers to give their best in the face of this challenge breaks any hold that their doubt may be exercising over their truth. In so doing, each rebirther grows.

Being aware of the synchronous connection in the rebirthing process gives the rebirther an extra channel of information and empathy. The rebirther's body and mind are registering reactions to the rebirthee as the rebirthee generates a heightened flow of energy during the session. The self–aware rebirther will use the feelings and thoughts that he or she has as clues to what may be happening with the rebirthee. Trusting both experience and intuition, the rebirther is then in a position to assist the rebirthee in releasing. Sometimes this assistance may be in the form of silently modeling a releasing thought or behavior, and sometimes the assistance may come by way of verbal instruction. In either case, the rebirther needs to be self–aware enough not to be projecting or assuming incorrectly what is happening for the rebirthee. I, as a rebirther, need to get my ego out of the way when it tries to show off how intuitive and right I am. Sometimes I am in doubt and I must simply ask the rebirthee what is going on. Sometimes I have a sense of rightness about what I think is happening for the rebirthee even when the rebirthee denies it. It may be that the rebirthee is not aware of everything that is being processed for them. It could be that either they are not ready to make it conscious or it is not appropriate to deal with at the moment. Again, as a rebirther, I must get any "need to be right" out of the way and affirm that the rebirthee is proceeding at the pace needed. If there really is something important for the rebirthee's process to be uncovered, it will surface at the appropriate time. For example, as a rebirther, I may sense a rebirthee's anger toward his or her mother. The rebirthee may deny having any such anger. I may begin to doubt and wonder whether it is me or the rebirthee who has "mother anger." I do not need to convince the rebirthee that I am right to alleviate my doubt. That is my problem. I need to affirm that if indeed there is anger on the rebirthee's part, it will surface when the rebirthee is ready. I can assist the rebirthee to get ready by increasing the medium of safety and comfort with feelings, but I am not about tricking the rebirthee into an admission that they are not ready to handle. In the meantime, I internally check out my own maternal anger quotient to see if I need some release. If so, my release will be a primary ingredient in creating safety for the rebirthee.

During the session, as a rebirther, I may get images of the rebirthee's past, present or future. These may be related to the issues the rebirthee is handling or releasing. It is not necessary for me to interpret or communicate these images. This may or may not be useful. It is my job to go beyond the image and affirm the loving intention behind it. Then, whether I am correctly seeing an element of their history or projecting a symptom of something I had for lunch, I am affirming the highest for the rebirthee. (In a synchronous universe it could be both.) I may, for example, have a mental flash of the rebirthee being beaten as a child. This may be something that actually happened in this or another lifetime, or something that the rebirthee feared happening, or something that happened emotionally rather than physically, or symbolic of what the rebirthee is doing to his or her inner child, or all or none of the above. I may or may not say something about this to the rebirthee during or after the session depending on how it may serve the process. What I will do for certain, however, is to affirm the rebirthee's safety, ability to release hurt and claim true loving strength. My faith is that seeing the image during the rebirthing was not accidental. To the degree that I continue breathing and supporting myself and the rebirthee, I help to release whatever pain or holding needs to be released on either of our parts. This faith creates the atmosphere which makes it easier for the rebirthee to do the same.

Knowing that all healing is taking place simultaneously allows me as a rebirther to give my best service as I receive it, learn as I teach, eliminate separation between me and others, see that my receiving is not selfish nor unprofessional nor even distracting from my task as a healer. It takes a certain level of certitude, confidence and self–esteem to receive as I give. Otherwise I think I am cheating others or unworthy to give. Holding on to these self–images replaces my joy with guilt and reduces the sense of clarity I transmit to others as a rebirther. With a synchronous, harmonious view of the world and mode of operation, I share rebirthing as a fellow–teacher and student with light beings who present the exact challenge I need for my growth as I serve theirs.

CLARITY

The rebirther's clarity of purpose, intentions and communications opens the door to effectiveness in results. This does not mean that the rebirther pretends to know it all on the conscious level. The rebirther does trust both his or her higher self as well as the healing process itself. This allows the rebirther to let go and risk on the ego level. The rebirther grows in the certitude of his or her healing process and uses every rebirth to learn and fine tune his or her intuitive senses.

BODY TYPES

Each rebirther learns through experience and creates a fund of knowledge from which to draw as well as trusts intuition in the process. I was a student of body energies and breathing even before I heard about rebirthing. I have used my knowledge of and training with body types through Alexander Lowen's *BIOENERGETICS*[1] to help systematize my observations about styles of breathing patterns. It is the mind and its pattern of thought which manifests into a body and its way of breathing. Knowing how major life themes become incorporated into physical form is an asset in both recognizing the themes and helping release them.

The following is a synopsis of the developmental stages and the body types presented more fully in *FAMILY AWAKENING*[2] and the breathing patterns associated with each. We all pass through each developmental stage and reach our own conclusions about the challenge we face at each level. As such, we all participate to some degree in each of the themes at each stage. Each of us generally chooses to focus on one of these themes more than others, however, as evidenced by the effect it has on the shaping and holding of our body patterns.

PSYCHIC SENSITIVE

This body type is developed from the conclusions reached about basic safety during pre– and post–natal periods of life. If I perceive coldness or hostility in my environment I may conclude that "I

[1] Lowen, A. BIOENERGETICS. NY: Coward, McCann & Geoghegan, 1975

[2] Morningstar, J. FAMILY AWAKENING.Milwaukee: Transformations Incorporated, 1984

am not safe here (in my body and in my world)." The body reflects this fear with chronic guardedness, a holding in of the musculature that promotes disjointedness and a seeming mechanical inhabitation of the flesh. Psychic Sensitives tend to avoid eye contact or stare through others because direct contact has been associated with danger. They feel vulnerable and sensitive to the physical, emotional and psychic environments, and are generally more comfortable in the mental and psychic realms. Consequently, they often try to fade into the background and not be noticed or try to "rise above it all." The Psychic Sensitive types breathe shallowly and minimally – just enough to sustain life, but not be seen or feel too deeply. They feel separate and keep themselves that way for their own protection, seldom making open or vulnerable contact. The challenge at this stage is to exist and get needs met at the same time. The goal in rebirthing with this theme is to increase the sense of inner safety. This is accomplished by increasing the capacity to safely experience aliveness as the individual learns to breathe fully. This requires providing a safe channel for expression and release of fear and anger sometimes to the point of rage. Frozeness in the chest is melted as the heart is released and the body becomes more supple, integrated and vibrant. The natural tendency toward spiritual and artistic expression of this style is now blended with a comfort with the material world, especially the bodily and heartfelt contact with other bodies. The rebirther's own sense of safety and genuine warmth, in the face of the fear and distancing this type portrays,is crucial at the onset of rebirthing.

Dan is aware of how his psychic sensitive style has permeated his life. His rebirthing reflects how awareness of his theme can lead to successful release and reunion.

DAN, AGE 38
THERAPIST

It started Saturday morning with a severe migraine headache (which I have learned forceps babies are prone to). I have a history of migraines, but I hadn't had one in several months and told Jim about this and at the same time showed him the scars on my head. He helped release the physical pain. But then, the emotional pain set in. I hadn't been aware of the hatred I had for the physical body. Of course, on an "intellectual level" it all made sense: difficult birth, struggle down the birth canal, trauma at entry. Pain! Pain! Pain! This has meant for me a life of creating situations to fit my birth experience. Pain. Always wanting to get out.

I had perfected this process of getting out. As a "Psychic Sensitive," I can leave the body at will. I know how to travel to different levels of consciousness freely without bodily harm and go into unity with God.

On the physical level, though, I don't know how to take good care of myself at all. My life habits on this level are unhealthy. But this is my program from birth.

So now, five years later at Green Lake, I relive the physical birth trauma. As I get in touch "with my head," the pain I associate with being in a body, the next phase is to release the physical trauma. So in a real sense, "I rebirth myself all over again."

As I began to breathe that morning, the body started out very mellow. I thought this would be another nice out of body trip as I had become accustomed to.

Unfortunately (or fortunately) this changed. My body began to reel and writhe with an intensity I had rarely experienced before. The anger and rage I felt at birth was ready to be released. As I continued to breathe, I "was there again" in my mother's womb. The struggle, fear and anger at not being able to get out. I twisted and turned with my struggle to be free – and breathed and breathed, until I was out at last, free to be – alive and well in a beautiful body.

Timing – readiness – peeling off the layers.

As always, for me the meaning of such experiences lies in the way I can integrate it into my daily life.

The Psychic Sensitive part of me is very useful. So is the physical. Now that I have "re–entered" my body, I strive towards a healthier integration of the two. For me this will, of course, mean I will continue to travel. Psychically – I must.

On the other hand, since my Green Lake rebirth, I feel more "real" in the body. I have come to accept the fact that the relationship will probably always be somewhat challenging. However, my intention is to reduce these polarities so that there is a greater sense of harmony and integration within all the parts of me.

EMPATHETIC NURTURING

During the first year of life, if I see myself as being deprived, I can conclude "I never get enough." The lack of ***Abundance*** in attention, food, time, etc.

becomes a major life theme. Learning to grow up and stand up for themselves quickly, the Empathetic Nurturing types become experts at taking care of others in hopes of appearing not needy while getting others to be supportive of them. Their bodies may be tall and thin with collapsed chest, pelvis forward, locked knees and unsupportive legs. Their heads, and particularly mouths, run the show. Oral needs predominate. Periods of high energy alternate with collapse, depressive feelings and/or sense of abandonment. The challenge at this stage is to get needs met and maintain independence at the same time. In rebirthing, the goal is to increase their genuine strength based on an inner sense of being their own source. This collapsed chest and impeded breathing has reinforced their sense of neediness on a breath by breath basis. They literally are supporting themselves on reduced breathing. They must learn in the process that they can tolerate and sustain higher energy levels without the expected abandonment and collapse. When their mood shifts or they do not get the supportive contact they expect, they learn not to abandon themselves or fall into depression. They begin to care for themselves like they used to care for others. They grow in the strength of their self–esteem and literally strengthen their lower body – their physical support system. Rather than needing to do it all at once (grow up fast), they learn to breathe more fully in a way they can maintain. Their caring and empathy are now based on a sharing from their abundance rather than a fear of lack.

The rebirther represents one who assists this growth without doing it for the Empathetic Nurturing rebirthee, i.e., without creating another dependency relationship which will always lead to being unable to fulfill their insatiable demands. The rebirther becomes a model for caring with clear agreements about expectations. The rebirther is not flattered into the position of the source of all good for the rebirthee who then ultimately fails to meet the rebirthee's needs. Rather, the rebirther assists the empathetic nurturing rebirthee to uncover the lie that he or she is not good enough, and dismiss the compensating belief of being the one who has got it together and needs no one. The rebirther's own sense of fullness and trust in the "source within" is invaluable in this process.

INSPIRATIONAL LEADER

Children, having adopted a level of safety and a conclusion about their abundance, encounter another challenge as they begin to move about and explore their environment during the first to third year of life. Who is in control of their behavior? Is it their inner drives or outer authorities? If I conclude that my needs are always being manipulated by others' rules, my relationships become a struggle for control. If the model for human interaction is domination and manipulation rather than ***Mutual Support and Harmony***, then I must always be on guard to maintain my position. My life becomes a struggle with authorities or a striving to be the authority. Two styles emerge from the resulting life theme "I must keep control." The first is an overpowering style which tries to dominate through intimidation and will power. The second is a seductive style which tries to gain control through manipulation. Both learn to suppress their feelings so as not to show vulnerability – "to give in to feeling is weak." If feelings are shown, they are for the purpose of controlling or gaining an advantage. The overpowering types develop large upper body proportions, especially head, shoulders and chest compared to their lower body, pelvis and legs. They must maintain their inflated ego image for fear of the underlying weakness of their own support system, psychologically not feeling valued by the authorities and physically weak in the legs. The seductive types have more even body proportions, but a tense inner musculature which is always on guard, sometimes with a hyperflexible back. They can be very affable, charming and persuasive, but never let you get to know the feelings behind their act. Often they have learned the role so well that they are not even aware of how defended they are.

The breathing pattern in these Inspirational Leader types differs from the first two body types described. Rather than being unable to take a deep breath as with the Psychic Sensitive, or to sustain full breathing as with the Empathetic Nurturing, their chests are inflated and their difficulty is being able to let down and exhale fully. They keep others away from their hearts literally and figuratively. The challenge at this stage is to maintain independence and have closeness at the same time. The positive goal here is to be able to pleasurably let down, be safe in letting go of tight control, receive support from others and not have to be continually on top. This is assisted in the relaxing and experiencing of feelings on their exhale. They learn to value their feelings rather than override or manipulate them as it seemed their early parenting figures did. They gain strength in their psychological and physical support systems. This is when their true leadership qualities blossom. They build upon their natural abilities to take charge with a relearned capacity to use their own and other's feelings to help them stay in touch as they give direction. Their spontaneity and verve is now based on inner security and is heartfelt. Their heads and their hearts are in balance and harmony, and this is reflected in their relationships which produce mutual satisfaction. The rebirther assists in being a model of an integrated authority who works with them rather than getting in a power struggle, whose strength is based on in–touchness rather than superiority, and who strives for mutual satisfaction rather than win/lose.

STEADFAST SUPPORTIVE

As children continue to develop in their abilities to master their behavior and their surroundings, so do they differentiate their feelings and emotional expressions during their second to fourth year of life. The variety of feelings they express and their ***Freedom of Expression*** enhance their interaction with their world. If some of these feelings are less accepted or threatening to important others in their lives, and they are humiliated for having them, they learn to suppress these feelings and associate them with a "bad me." Eventually, what becomes acceptable to them is only the "good me" feelings and behaviors which were rewarded by the important others, i.e., parents, teachers. Anger and frustration are held in. This presents a pattern of compliance outwardly and resistance inwardly. The body is, looks and feels bound in and squashed. Their bodies appear more massive with thick neck, barrel chest, waist short and heavy, pelvis tucked in (held from bottom) and thighs and calves overdeveloped. Steadfast Supportive types become experts at taking in everyone's expectations, but letting out very little of their true expression. Anger comes out indirectly as whining, complaining or provoking. Their internal pressure is experienced as a morass of struggle. Their efforts to please and be a "good boy" or "good girl" only produce temporary relief until the theme of "No one appreciates me" and "I must struggle to get what I want" are unmasked and reversed. The challenge at this stage is to maintain closeness and to have freedom of expression at the same time. When they learn to reown and channel the emotional energy that had been repressed, they literally learn to breathe easier. Again, as with the Inspirational Leaders, they must learn to let go on the exhale and release their expanded chest. Rather than struggling to please the rebirther, they learn to breathe for themselves. This releases their creative, playful spirits and their bodies take on a lightness and softness. These positive qualities of endurance and helpfulness to others are now balanced with a self–care and self–acceptance. As they value and appreciate all of who they are, integrating the former "bad me" feelings into more straight–forward assertiveness, they appreciate themselves in a new way. Consequently, they get more appreciation for all sides of them, not just the "approval seeking" parts. The rebirther helps them experience and express their feelings in a responsible and effective way. This takes staying in touch with their feelings on a breath by breath basis and trusting the loving intention behind each feeling.

GENDER BALANCED

Between the third and fifth year of life, children begin to formalize their sex–role attitudes and behaviors and to seek ***Sexual Integration.*** With greater differentiation of their sensory and motor abilities comes also a greater awareness of genital vs. non–genital sensations and behaviors. If this development is threatening to their parents and themselves, they may go into collusion in fostering mixed messages about their sexual roles. Their conflict is that to express their natural initiative, to maintain their freedom of expression, seems to threaten their gender identity. As protection, they develop an unbalanced or exaggerated mode of expression. Their sexual preference may be heterosexual or homosexual, but the male Gender Balanced types originally adapt a passive–feminine role, and the female adopts a masculine–aggressive role. This is not just a simple departure from cultural stereotypes. The belief is that "if I accept myself spontaneously I will be rejected." This patterning produces a man who is fearful of any direct or natural assertiveness, who must operate more with guile and cunning to undermine opposition. His body pattern is generally soft and rounded on the outside while hard and rigid on the inside. His movements are never brusque and his expression is more soft and plastic. His illusion is that he will be safe as long as he is not overly aggressive.

The female pattern is fear of softness or vulnerability, resulting in an over–emphasis on aggressiveness and especially competitiveness with males. Her body is split between top and bottom being rigid and tight in the one and more weak and undercharged in the other. A sensitive child–like quality alternates with rebellion and attack under stress. Her illusion is that to show softness is to be devalued. Both male and female types think their own style is safer (less vulnerable) than others of their gender until they release their defensive posture. Balancing the inhale with the exhale in a smooth rhythm leads to their feelings and their expression becoming unified for both male and female types. The rebirther becomes a model for the acceptance and release of their repressed fears. They can recover the side of their spontaneous expressiveness that has been held back, while retaining the strengths they have developed. The Gender Balanced male retains his sensitivity and adaptiveness without being afraid of experiencing his strength. The Gender Balanced female keeps her assertion and directness without fearing her ability to let down and let in safely. The breath very visibly helps balance the inside with the outside and the top with the bottom of the gender balanced types. With the inner union of their male and female qualities being more complete, their relationships take on more balance and harmony and less distrust and competition with their partners. This marriage of male and female qualities allows the Gender Balanced types a very impactful creative expression through their sensitivity to the nuances of the masculine/feminine (Yang/Yin) dance in the universe.

ENERGETIC GROUNDED

Given that children have established a somewhat integrated sex–role identity between the ages of four to six, they begin to experiment with establishing relationships based on this new sense of self. They may have been encouraged to express themselves as an autonomous being in their environment. When it comes to forming an intimate relationship with an opposite–sex parent or parent substitute, however, a new challenge arises. A child's natural desire to express his or herself fully with his or her new identity, and seek ***Intimacy***, can become a threat that, when handled defensively on both parts, leads to the appearance of betrayal and rejection. The girl, for example, who has always been "Daddy's little darling," suddenly is no longer allowed to sit on his lap and who is treated with fear and distancing around sexual feelings, may subconsciously conclude that sex and love never go together. The Energetic

Grounded types learn to channel their abundant energy into productive pursuits and often become quite successful in dealing with the world. They are able to blow off steam when they need to. When a relationship becomes more than a challenge or conquest, though, the split between their heart and their genitals surfaces. The male body pattern is of fairly even proportions with a rigid back, raised squared–off shoulders, set jaw and bright eyes that make good contact. The female also portrays strength, energy and rigidity in fairly even body proportions. Their illusion is that they are free as long as they do not surrender to love – "no one is going to hurt me again." Attempting to maintain intimacy resurrects this lie that something is wrong with them and despite their success in other areas, they cannot have a full, loving, sexual relationship. Their challenge is to maintain their gender identity while being able to surrender to love. The male may mask his fears behind bravado and handle his intimacy through acting out a "madonna/prostitute syndrome," giving his heart to his wife but his sexuality to someone he does not love.

The female may vacillate between periods of relative promiscuity and then frigidity, hoping for her ideal lover who will reunite her split between tender heartfelt emotion and sensuality. She seeks excitement and romance to break through the rigidity, but blocks the full experience of love so she will not be hurt. The Energetic Grounded types may readily learn and follow the rebirthing technique externally, but also cleverly avoid surrendering to the feelings of

BODY TYPE (AGE) DEVELOPMENTAL CHALLENGE	NEGATIVE PERCEPTION vs. UNDERLYING TRUTH	BASIC BELIEF COMPENSATING BELIEF	FROZEN BODY IMAGE INTEGRATED BODY IMAGE
PSYCHIC SENSITIVE (PRE–POSTNATAL) Existence vs. need	Coldness and hostility vs. Sensitivity and safety	"The world (my body) is not a safe place…" "I am a free spirit unattached to the material."	Disjointed, frozen; minimal breathing; unfocused. High vibrational; agile; artistically proficient; responsive.
EMPATHETIC LEADER (1ST YEAR) Need vs. independence	Deprivation vs. Abundance	"I'll never get enough" "If I love enough I'll be loved." or "I'm self–sufficient."	Shallow inhale; collapsed chest; pelvis forward; knees locked; often tall and thin. Light; approachable; warm, yielding; receptive.
INSPIRITIONAL LEADER (1ST – 3RD YEAR) Independence vs. closeness	Overpowering or seduction vs Mutual support and harmony	"To give in to feeling weak." "I'm in control."	Muscle bound, upper body inflated or normal proportions with hyperflexible back. Strong attractive, energy up.
STEADFAST SUPPORTIVE (2ND – 4TH YEAR) Closeness vs. Freedom of expression	Humiliation vs. Freedom of expression and respect.	"No one appreciates me." "My struggle is noble."	Thick neck; pelvis tucked in; waist short and thick,; often squashed appearance. Solid; enduring; tender; huggable.
GENDER BALANCED (3RD – 5TH YEAR) Freedom of expression vs. gender identity	Role confusion vs. Sexual integration	"If I assert myself spontaneously, I will be rejected." "My assertion is safer than others' of my gender."	Male–soft rounded exterior; compliant expression. Female–split upper and lower body–one rigid, the other weak; tight jaw. Integrated inner and outer, upper and lower, balance assertion and sensitivity.
ENERGETIC GROUNDED (4TH – 6TH YEAR) Gender Identity vs. Surrender to love	Disappointment vs. Intimacy	"No one is going to hurt me again." "I'm a loving person who no one understands."	Armored; stiff back; eyes bright. Attractive; alert; capable; healthy.

REACTION TO STRESS STRENGTH	REBIRTHING GOALS	AFFIRMATIONS
SPLIT OFF SENSITIVITY	Increase breathing and safety in experiencing Release rage and fear. Gain comfort with body.	I need not be afraid of anything inside of me. I'm safe when I feel my feelings. I'm welcome here. My body is a perfect vehicle for the expression of my love and light.
COLLAPSE EMPATHY	Increase self–support and ability to sustain experiences of aliveness over time. Decrease abandonment and depletion themes.	It's OK to need. I'll never abandon myself. I now attract all the support I need to fulfill all my desires. I do enough, I have enough, I am enough.
CONTROL, RISE ABOVE, SEDUCE LEADERSHIP Release exhale.	Increase pleasure in letting go. Surrender with others, Safety and pleasure in feelings.	I'm a good person. I'm important to myself and others. It's safe for me to feel vulnerable. I safely experience and express all my feelings. It's enjoyable to let others support me.
PROVOKE HELPING	Complete exhale. Deal directly with anger and release the creative spirit.	My anger is my love. I no longer have to struggle and be good to get what I want. My anger always leads to increased joy and intimacy. I now openly receive the acknowledgement and appreciation I've always wanted.
(M) UNDERMINE (F) ATTACK BLEND MALE AND FEMALE PERSPECTIVES	Balance inhale and exhale, strength and sensitivity. Accept safety in sexual identity.	My sexuality is holy; my sexual expression leads to increase intimacy, understanding and love in my life. I accept and enjoy my male and female qualities. I am an attractive, loving man (woman) and I express my life energy fully, freely and pleasurably.
BLOW OFF DEAL EFFECTIVELY WITH THE WORLD.	Integrate inhale and exhale Unite love and sexuality. Safety in vulnerability with others.	Opening my heart always leads to greater experience of love and safety. Expressing my true feelings and desires always leads to increased intimacy. I forgive myself for believing that I was rejected sexually. I now attract relationships that are both loving and sexual fulfilling.

hurt, anger and fear associated with the "betrayal." This betrayal may have been enacted with a parent who loved them, but seemed to reject their sexuality. The feelings are kept present through the betrayal within themselves by a body and mind that rigidly holds out love. The rebirther assists the release of the illusion that the energetic grounded is a loving person that no one understands. When the fear of hurt is faced and the inner betrayal unmasked, the Energetic Grounded individual is more supple and open to receive love as well as be accomplished in life. The heart and the genitals can be united in intimacy. Their breathing moves energy from head to toe. The inhale and exhale are integrated, not just performed well, and reflects the integration of their strength and surrender. Then attractive, alert, capable qualities shine forth with warmth and openness. Rebirthing provides a powerful and compelling enough concentration of spiritual flow to help dissolve the resistance to an integrated experience of love. The rebirther must enlist the Energetic Grounded into a mutual effort toward their goal rather than be lulled into a competitive test of competency or a reenactment of the betrayal/disappointment drama.

Each of us passes through each of these early life stages, faces the challenges inherent in them and adapts our postures toward them. As a rebirther, I do not see rebirthees as body types. I see each rebirthee as a unique seeker of fulfillment who has also faced common challenges in the formation of their mind and body on this planet. The body types can be a useful reference in uncovering their personal laws, the themes which bear most relevance on their particular path. No two individuals blend their themes in exactly the same way, nor do they breathe them into their bodies in the same fashion. As a rebirther, I use body types only inasmuch as they assist me in seeing through the personality to the truth of the divine being who created it. Each body type has its strengths and they are to be built upon in the process of freeing the rebirthee's creative potential. In this regard, it is the rebirther's job to know his or her own body type and personal laws in order not to trip over them or project them wholesale onto their rebirthees. I consider it unwise to use any technique or tool with others until I have used it on myself. There is no substitute for self–awareness and self–acceptance in training as a rebirther.

PROFESSIONAL TRAINING AND APPLICATION

I work with and train many professionals in the use of rebirthing. I am delighted to share my rebirthing with others whom I know will adapt it to their needs and share it with those they serve. This may be as direct as actually practicing the rebirthing technique as a professional rebirther to simply using it personally and being an example of integrated breathing without ever mentioning it to others.

Those in medical fields from physicians to physical and occupational therapists have used awareness of the principles of connected breathing while they are treating others to assist in the healing process. They will both teach more open breathing to their patients and/or refer them to a rebirther when appropriate. Those in the field of psychotherapy have also integrated open connected breathing into their work from use in visualization, and stress reduction to actual rebirthing sessions in the course of therapy. Educators have employed the principles of mind/body work in the learning process, knowing that an energetically open body is more receptive. This was demonstrated by a teacher who had her class do some breathing exercises every day before the lessons began to a principal who taught "naughty" children sent out of the classroom to her how to breathe and center themselves as they lay on a cot in her office.

Many business people have used rebirthing, both for their personal clearing and to assist their corporate climate. Some have referred key employees for rebirthing when they have shown an openness to this kind of learning. Others have used the process extensively to break through creative blocks and increase the quality of service and productivity in their work.

Every profession involves human interaction, agreements, services and/or products exchanged. The use of conscious connected breathing as an adjunct to how you do your work is very powerful. It is up to each individual to develop the method which works best in using these skills. I most simply begin and end each day with clearing connected breathing.

This is my most effective business practice. I often eliminate hours of work by gaining clarity within myself before I start my day. I discover tasks that really do not need to be done or that might better be done by someone else. Coming to my work with freshness and energy makes a vast difference both in what I put into it and what I get out of it.

SCHOOLS OF BREATHING

Rebirthing is a vehicle en route to breath and body mastery, that state of consciously creating with each breath. There are many time–honored schools of thought and programs of training dedicated to this purpose. Some of these schools have very specific instructions for their students with graduated steps for their progress. Questions arise for the serious student as to which is the best school with the best techniques. I believe each must find the one suited to his or her path.

Some yogic traditions advocate nose and diaphramatic breathing and may appear in contradiction to the mouth and costal (chest) breathing that I often use at the beginning of rebirthing. The nose and diaphragm breathing highlights more parasympathetic activities in the body and helps generate the meditative, peaceful state that these forms of yoga seek. There are other forms of yoga, however, that use the "breath of fire" and are identical in many ways to the initial rebirthing techniques. The student of yoga ultimately must decide which yogic breath is best for them at which point in their life.

I use the very active chest breathing (panting breath) only when the rebirthee has established enough safety in the process that they are able to stay balanced as they "ride the waves" of energy that they generate. After a significant release in the emotional holding assisted by their sympathetic nervous system activation, there comes a more even balance between sides of the brain and the body as well as the psyche. At this point, the entire body of the rebirthee is breathing as one motion, a wave initiated in their center and spreading out in all directions from head to toe. This is the breath of the peaceful baby. The rebirthee may be breathing through his or her nose or mouth. They are breathing with harmony from their source.

Those body types with less physical armoring, i.e., the Psychic Sensitive and the Empathetic Nurturing, will generally find the mouth breathing more immediately stimulating and therefore threatening. They find it difficult to sustain vigorous breathing over a long period. It is necessary to calibrate the breath to the individual body type, to let the rebirthee breathe at the rate which their body can tolerate, and to increase this tolerance at a pace that is right for their system.

ESTABLISHING A PRACTICE IN REBIRTHING

For those who are called to be rebirthers, who have been trained and who want to start their own practice, I recommend the following steps:

First clarify your intentions in the use of rebirthing for yourself and your rebirthees. I see rebirthing as not curing others, but rather giving them the tool to open their awareness to their inner self–healing ability. Secondly, be honest about who you want to rebirth and under what circumstances: whom you wish to have as rebirthees, how often, where, whether you want to establish a profession and have a fee, and how you want to let others know you are available. All these may be unknowns at the onset, but continuing to be honest with yourself about what is your heart's desire helps to manifest results more readily. Third, exercise your responsibility to yourself on a regular basis for your own growth, your own rebirthing, body work, relationships, etc. Make these same opportunities available to your rebirthees by making them aware of the resources around them, e.g., books, tapes, healing techniques, trainings. Help create a support network for those going through the rebirthing process. This may take the form of seminars, groups, or some kind of events which bring rebirthees together in a supportive atmosphere. We all need nurturance for changes in consciousness. Encourage supportive connection among rebirthees, eventually exchanging rebirthings with each other. Be willing to encourage those who themselves want to pursue a rebirthing career. This is planetary clearing and the earth is grateful. We all win as the spirit of breath is promoted.

Rebirthing is a highly adaptable skill in terms of creating a profession. Massage therapists, psychotherapists, school principals, artists, financial advisors, carpenters and others have all integrated the use of rebirthing into their careers. Each has discovered the meaning of rebirthing for themselves and then have been willing to share its value with others.

THE CIRCLE OF GUIDES

The most continuous and extensive training I receive in rebirthing comes through the inner guidance developed in my personal breathwork. As I breathe each evening in water, I put attention on and asked for assistance in my life and my work. Gradually over the years various teachers came to me, not in the sense of physical apparitions, but more of internal voices of guidance. I began to access and use their guidance during my breathing sessions each morning and evening. My sense of this was assembling a circle of guides habitually whenever I did connected breathing and soliciting their input and support. Sometimes this would be direct and forceful, at other times it would be just background support. I found that if I was willing to develop these relationships they could become more concrete and directly useful in dealing with my life challenges. This was not a process of giving my power away and listening for someone else to give me my answers. It was more opening to confirm truths that were already within me and reminding me of what I already knew. These guides are with me always in spirit as I work and play. They become a reminder of my creative source. I invoke their assistance especially as I rebirth others and I suggest that they work together with the supportive guidance of those with whom I work. I invite you to breathe with and discover your own circle of guides and rebirth teachers.

Listening to and using their guidance will change your way of life and way of helping others.

ANA, AGE 33
NURSE

The most significant rebirth for me was on 1/17/87. I awoke and was told by an inner voice to come right home after work although I had an appointment. I rebirthed myself in a reclining chair at work recalling the Ah! sound as a tone used in a chant to awaken the heart, and I used an Ah! sound in breathing and it centered my breath in my chest. It was very easy to feel the breath in my chest. It was very easy to feel the breath move in and out of my chest and focus there. A powerful release of energy surged through my body, tremors. Slight choking and body jerked as if throwing off a plug. I then felt a warm flood and flow of energy.

I attempted to keep my appointment and after driving for two hours and being unable to find my friends house I followed the morning's message to go home. I had to laugh at being unable to get to my destination since I am a frequent visitor there. I arrived home and desire to rebirth myself came up. I used the sound again and my breath immediately went to heart region. Sadness filled me and I remembered my affirmation," I use my sorrow with an open heart. It leads me to rediscover more fully that which I thought was lost." I followed the sorrow and continued with Ah! connected breathing and a rapid release followed by a presence who is to be my son. This presence told me many, many things. I saw a vivid picture of him. I in the past have had contact with him; but not as clear and direct as this.

The ultimate trainer in rebirthing is the spirit of breath in each person. We are here to assist each other in hearing this spirit. I help train rebirthers at Transformations Incorporated in Milwaukee, Wisconsin. It is one of the joys of my life.

CHAPTER SIX

THE BIRTH OF TRANSFORMATIONS INCORPORATED AND COMMUNITY REBIRTHING AT REBIRTH TRAININGS

THE MISSION

As the name implies, Transformations Incorporated is a center for rebirthing dedicated to embodying changes. The Latin roots of the words signify "changing of form" and "putting in a body." The mission of this Midwest based Center, which began in the early 1980's, is to offer transformative experience that will make an observable difference in people's physical existence. The body is not seen as a second class citizen in the realm of spiritual work. Our intent is not to glorify the physical, but to truly transform it such that it becomes a fitting vehicle for spiritual truth. Instead of living for the body or living to eliminate it, the direction is to change our attitudes and perceptions of it, the instructions we give to it and, finally, the quality of its very substance. Through the transformation of rebirthing, we at once affirm our unity with the Spiritual Source and begin to live fully in our light bodies, without having to destroy our physical bodies in the process.

Those who began this venture were both professionals and non–professionals, but all were students of the spirit and teachers of the heart. Transformations now includes a state licensed counseling center and a school for spiritual development and training. Each person involved in its creation has his or her own transformational journey which has synchronously come together with the others. The following is an account of my personal call to rebirthing. It is one example of how the spirit of breath keeps preparing us for the next stage of growth through all life experiences.

THE CALL TO REBIRTHING

I did not find in the rebirthing movement a long history of tradition or an established body of teaching nor hierarchy of teachers. In the early 1970's, Leonard Orr and a handful of fellow explorers from around the country were rediscovering power of the breath combined with the practice of universal principles of creative thought.[1] The consciousness of the planet was ready for larger breakthroughs by greater numbers of people and this was a vehicle for such a

[1] Orr L. and Ray S. REBIRTHING IN THE NEW AGE. Millbrae, CA: Celestial Arts, 1977

movement. Of course, many other schools of personal growth, some newly founded, others renovated, were and still are promoting the awareness and responsibility necessary for a new level integration in mind, body and spirit. Rebirthing, though, provided for me the most elegant and simple tool for physical and mental transformation. This has been adopted in some form by many other schools, and so it should be. The newly evolving rebirthing movement went about presenting the technique and the philosophy in a way that would reach those who were ready for its use. The profoundly moving home birth of our second child, Sam, seemed to open the door for me to be rebirthed and to share this joyous process with others. After having gone through my own rebirthing, I was quickly initiated into being a rebirther. I had been leading groups that involved deep breathing and during one of these, my clients started to go into spontaneous rebirths. I later surmised this was because of my new state of openness. Nonetheless, I had to decide immediately whether to encourage and assist them or to draw back and plead ignorance. For me there was no choice but to move forward. My own personal evolution seemed to depend upon my willingness to teach. This type of teaching was not from my head, however. Rebirthing seemed to require more of getting my thoughts out of the way and letting a "higher me" facilitate the healing. Success in facilitating others was success in clearing myself and giving my highest service.

ONE YEAR SEMINARS

Taking responsibility for making mind and body a moment–by–moment vehicle for the divine and using the breath as a tool in this process began to bring people together. They wanted to learn and be with others who were also willing to take such powerful and definitive steps. Seminar series were formed to create the atmosphere to allow individuals to integrate new ways of thinking and breathing over extended periods. These seminars met for an entire day once a month for a year. The power of rebirthing was that it allowed me to experience myself as the creator of my life, not just to know it intellectually. Like any other experience, it can be denied and eventually buried under doubt unless it is nourished and practiced. These One Year Seminar programs allowed us to reinforce our new experience of Self in a wide variety of mental and emotional conditions. We were then encouraged to take our responsible selves out of the seminar setting into daily life. Our breath became both a reminder and a technique to bring us back to the experience of being in charge of our lives rather than a victim of circumstances.

Since this style of work was most appealing to me, I did all of the training and practice I could absorb. My family participated in their own rebirthing process and supported mine. This often involved traveling around the country to attend workshops. I attended the national certification training out of both my attraction to the process and my desire to achieve. All of my old logical approaches to achievement, however, got in the way rather than assisted me. The process of certification required a high level of trust in intuition and release of the ego in the face of the higher truth. In the midst of feeling like a complete failure, it was only a voice inside that suggested that if I could support myself in the face of total humiliation then I was certifying myself. It is only when I acknowledged my true self that recognition by others means anything. I feel grateful to those who assisted me in this process.

I became director of Theta International which coordinated One Year Seminar programs around the U.S. and Canada. This long–term education was dearest to my heart because I believe it helped effect long–term changes in people. I traveled extensively during this period and found that the same spiritual community existed everywhere despite having seemingly different faces. This phase of my apprenticeship drew to a close after two years. It became apparent that I now needed to sink in roots in order to give greater support to the extending branches of the rebirthing movement.

THE SCHOOL OF SPIRITUAL PSYCHOLOGY

I had been conducting several OYS programs in Milwaukee and some of the graduates were now looking for more advanced spiritual work. From this impetus came the School of Spiritual Psychology. Each step involved my reaching deeper into myself and sharing more on the one hand while letting go and allowing it to evolve on the other. The OYS was shortened to six months and is now called the Creative Life Series (CLS). An intensive six month Personal Integration Program was formed which included the CLS, as well as an 18 session body mastery training (Body Aliveness Series), an 18 session process group in which everyone's emotional autobiography is shared (Core Group), two residential weekend intensives and personal consultations for physical, mental and spiritual well–being. The Personal Integration Program is designed to allow participants to carry on their occupation and family life and apply what they are learning immediately in these settings. The PIP continues to amaze me in the intensity and permanency of positive life change that it stimulates.

When there were enough PIP graduates, a Spiritual Leadership Program (SLP) was formed. The PIP is an intensive interior exploration. The SLP uses the higher level of personal energy generated within the PIP graduates and directs it toward expressing spiritual leadership in the world. This translates, for the participants, into creating natural forms of expressing the truth of who they are in their daily life. This involves increasing the mastery within their social and business relationships as well as exploring leadership in the world of their dreams. Those who practice this level of leadership for a year and who are ready to commit themselves fully to the life of a present day mystic become apprenticed for their third year in the School of Spiritual Psychology. In the

Graduate Apprenticeship Program, they focus on honing skills in their chosen profession in such a way as to maximize their spiritual evolution. Successful completion of three years of dedication to conscious growth is acknowledged by a Master of Spiritual Psychology Certificate. This is an outer sign of an inner self–awarded mastery.

Some graduates of the School major in the healing arts and many use rebirthing as one of their professional tools. Others direct their leadership to the business world and major in areas of holistic entrepreneurship offered in the School. Others concentrate on family or social relationships in how they manifest their path. The philosophy of creative thought is central to all and the rebirthing technique remains a guiding light for the creative experience.

TRANSFORMATIONS INCORPORATED

The faculty for the *SCHOOL OF SPIRITUAL PSYCHOLOGY* (SSP) has grown with the demand for advanced work and the arrival of the right teachers. Many of these teachers have gone through the programs themselves and know it from the inside out.

While the SSP was being developed, a group of spiritually oriented psychotherapists began working together through the newly established Transformations Incorporated. They formed the *CREATIVE CONSULTING AND COUNSELING SERVICES* (cccs) a State licensed outpatient counseling center. Through

CCCS, individuals in life crisis or involved in long–term challenges could discover how their stumbling blocks could become stepping stones to their next stage of growth. Many individuals who came to CCCS with negative self–image, found the emotional and metaphysical keys to unlock their misery and turn it into soul–quenching energy. They then proceeded to follow through with their growth in the SSP. I believe that most "emotional disorder" comes from life energy that is thwarted in its natural growth process and turns to dis–ease. When the channels for expression are opened, that very same energy, which was pain when it was blocked, is experienced as purposeful and pleasurable when released. The therapists at CCCS are not interested in "getting rid of problems," but rather in transforming misdirected energy into its original life–affirming state.

As with any organization, the growing consciousness of the individuals involved produces the challenges out of which each person must reach new heights and depths. It has only been through the courage, dedication and vision of the staff members that the opportunities have manifest into realities. Because they have gone for their highest potential, they have allowed their greatest fears to appear and summoned forth greater faith and strength to meet them.

It is the vision of *TRANSFORMATIONS* to be a model and a beacon. The model is of individuals dedicated to bringing out the whole student and teacher within them and to creating the vehicle through which they can learn, grow and share their highest with their world. The beacon is for those individuals who want to rekindle or nourish the light within them, to see the divine and to live in the truth as they dispel the darkness and illusion from their lives. This beacon is also intended to shine outwards to the worlds beyond as a testimonial to our love of the light and the breath of life.

COMMUNITY REBIRTHING AT REBIRTH TRAININGS

The Spirit of Breath calls people together for the purpose of sharing lessons in conscious evolution. These gatherings can be anything from chance encounters to lifelong friendships. The work of Transformations Incorporated is to use the model of creative thought in bringing people together with the conscious intention of furthering mutual growth. Besides the School of Spiritual Psychology programs already described, semi–annual rebirth trainings provide a powerful example of how the Spirit of Breath heals when a group of individuals is dedicated to this purpose.

Ciri used the safety and loving energy generated by the community attending a Rebirth Training to validate and reunite with a source of guidance first contacted in her childhood.

CIRI, AGE 45
CLAIMS PROCESSOR

As a child of eight years old, I was sitting on the back porch caught up in a day dream about what adventures would happen on that sunny, summer day. I looked up and saw a vision appear, from what seemed to come out of light, a life size being with a deep purple robe and a glow around Him. I recognized Him as Jesus.

My response was calm and I felt happy to see Him. I remember speaking aloud, "Oh, you're Jesus." The vision said nothing. He simply held out His arms. His eyes spoke of so much love for me. A few moments passed and the vision dissolved. I sat for a time and wondered why Jesus came to see me. I can still recall the vision as if it happened yesterday.

We did not attend a church, nor did we belong to one at that time. As time moved me into my adult years, I have often wondered what this unusual experience meant. Thinking back to that time now, I remember thinking either everyone has this experience and never talks about it, or no one does and I might be considered strange. I felt it best not to tell anyone of this "happening."

Thirty years passed; I was attending a Rebirth Training . During my rebirth, I found myself processing a lot of anger and disappointment that I had held on to from my childhood and family life. I suddenly became aware of a presence. The very same vision came into my consciousness. Once again, the very same loving eyes were focused on mine.

Almost immediately I became that very same eight year old child on the porch. This time the outstretched arms beckoned me towards Him. I found myself safely tucked under His arm as we turned and walked towards the wooded land which surrounded our house.

As we walked, my head resting on His chest and His arm securely around my shoulder, I had the sense that I was remembering and reviewing my life thus far here on earth. We walked for some time; the sun warmed us. I remember feeling the dry dirt from the old path "poofing" up from between my toes leaving little spots on the top of my feet.

Without words we seemed to speak with one another. This wonderful being seemed to be saying, "Ciri, all of what you have experienced in your life has been provided for you. Sanctuary in Mother Nature was a protection given you. What you call loneliness was your time to have communion with the animals, plants, birds and insects which you now understand and love so well. Look at the blessings in all of that."

In what was a timeless experience, we "spoke" of many subjects. What I came to know is a true loving forgiveness of others, an awareness of how everything is perfect and most significantly, we are never alone.

HOW THE REBIRTH TRAINING WORKS

Each rebirthing training has a different theme. Each gathering creates a different model community which lives, eats, works, plays and breathes together for a three day period. The energy generated from such a concentration of breathers whose intention is in alignment is quite powerful.

Participants draw on a psychic level to their training the exact group of individuals they need to further their own healing and growth. This provides them with the opportunity to deal with their fears, projections and illusions as well as their inner truth and source of wisdom, and to separate the illusions from the truth. This is the premise upon which the participants interact. The heightened energy serves to magnify what each person brings with them into the training. The avowed intention of each person is to clear themselves and be an instrument of clearing for others. The magnification allows each person to see more clearly how their thoughts and behaviors lend to harmony or disharmony, internally and externally.

Rebirth Training participants do not self–consciously spend the weekend analyzing themselves. On the contrary, the schedule provides a variety of exercises to be done individually, with a small group or with the entire community as well as time for contact with nature, reflection, sharing and play. In the course of these activities, each person's life patterns and attitudes emerge. This is not unfortunate, nor does it get in the way of the program. In fact, it is part of the program. The objective is to accept what arises in my thoughts and feelings, to notice its effect, and then to reach different conclusions about myself and the world if its effects are not life–affirming. The atmosphere of support and seeing others do this makes the success rate high in this process. As a very simple example, I may ask someone to walk to dinner with me and find that that person had already arranged to walk with someone else during this time.

My tendency may be to feel sad and conclude that I am not OK. Seeing that every minute is part of the training, however, I am encouraged to experience the temporary sadness, to conclude that I am OK and to be open to something else quite valuable during my walk to dinner. This "something else quite valuable" may be another person I meet on the way or perhaps a sense of loneliness that I needed to face and release.

THE ROLE OF REBIRTHING

Rebirthing is a central part of the Training and is practiced every day. Having a large group do this together seems to exponentially increase the available energy. Since it is the loving intention of the breather which powers the rebirth, and since there is lots of loving intention in the atmosphere, the "charge" builds within the community as they breathe each day throughout the weekend. If I choose, I can use this charge to take me through layers of resistance to expressing my love more completely. I can also resist this energy. To do it, however, I must reinforce old limitations and this is innately uncomfortable. My body provides its own feedback system and gives the motivation to seek release.

Release may be a quiet self–confident sense of increased acceptance, or it may come in the form of an emotional catharsis. I may find myself crying or experiencing fear or anger. This is my opportunity to release feelings that I may have repressed for years. Perhaps every time I experienced them in the past, I judged them and concluded something negative about myself, e.g. "I am bad if I feel anger" or "I am weak if I feel fear." These feelings are simply life energy seeking a natural flow and will always lead to harmony if given the opportunity and motivated with a loving intention. In my rebirthing I am encouraged to feel and to reach more positive conclusions, e.g. "My anger tells me I am not getting something I want and gives me the energy to go for it more successfully."

Randee shares how her rebirthing helped her deal with profound emotions she carried with her to the Training.

RANDEE, AGE 36
REAL ESTATE

In February, 1986, I was quite a novice at this rebirthing stuff. I had done it a few times with Jim in private sessions but never with anyone else. On Saturday morning of the Rebirth Training we paired ourselves up. We novices were given the opportunity to pick a partner who had much more experience. Connie and I chose each other. We were roomies for the weekend and it seemed right. After talking for a while in front of the warm fireplace, I felt comfortable enough to start. Connie let me know that whatever would happen, I would be safe, and I trusted her. Back in our room I started breathing. It didn't take long before I was in a good breathing pattern and I started drifting. I found myself in the middle of a storm of sadness – lots of tears, intense crying for what seemed like a very long time.

When the tears subsided, I found myself talking to the spirit of the baby I had just lost/given back to God. (I gave my baby's spirit my full attention because I felt he was really there with me.) I told him I just couldn't be his mother right now. I wasn't ready to care for him and love him in my life right now. I was so sad that I couldn't, but he seemed to understand, to say that he knew that was true. I told him I wished I could have kept him with me and that someday I would be ready to have him be my child, to love and care for him as I felt I couldn't at the time he felt ready. He seemed to understand and to love me all the same. And he was gone.

When I came back to consciousness, slowly and gently, I realized that he may not be here and ready to be my child when I was ready. But he needed to go on and so did I. Perhaps we would meet again in this life, perhaps in another and maybe we won't even know.

When I opened my eyes, Connie was there holding my arm. She came onto the bed with me and let me hold her like I would a child. I told her what I'd experienced and we held each other quietly and lovingly. This was a very special moment.

THE ORIGINS OF GROUP PROCESS

In the Rebirth Training setting all is directed toward release of anything that is not life–affirming. The measure of what is life–affirming is internal as opposed to anyone else's list of rules or standards. I believe there is a common suspicion of group settings, especially in which high energy processing takes place. I think this often stems back to our first group experience – birth. I came into this group setting which included at least my mother and frequently a doctor, nurses, anesthesiologist, or possibly a midwife, cab driver, etc. I was the most vulnerable member and often the least considered human. My needs and wants were seen through someone else's ideas of what they should be, i.e., hospital standards, medical practice, legal requirements, parental expectations. I felt fear and adopted a position of powerlessness. "The big guys (authorities) are running the show." I operate in future group settings, e.g., the family, church, school, reinforcing the conclusion that someone else is in power and my feelings are secondary. The Green Lake group process, for example, is not consciously decided by me, the participant, just as I was not verbally consulted by the doctor at birth about the technique of delivery I preferred. This does not mean that I am a helpless victim, however, neither then nor now.

PSYCHIC CONNECTEDNESS

I said there was no conscious consultation with me about my birth or most subsequent group participation. Every group I enter, however, I do so first on a level of psychic connectedness. This includes choosing my parents, on some level, for a specific purpose and it continues with every group I join. Each member of my group provides a specific healing and growth producing opportunity if I see the divine beneath the apparent illusion. As the time for the Training approaches there is being formed a psychic connection and agreement among the prospective participants. Very little of this is happening on the conscious level, but some of it is. I do openly solicit input from the School of Spiritual Psychology members and others. I listen carefully and get input from varied and sundry sources. Meanwhile, the planning for the training is going on and the psychic input from every future participant is helping to create the final form. You assist in creating every group you have ever entered, including agreeing beforehand to all the rules and regulations you subsequently buck up against. You draw in these challenges to eventually recognize and reaffirm your own authority, to see your own hand on the controls of the universe and enjoy it increasingly. At the Rebirth Training, this psychic process is simply recognized and acknowledged more openly.

REOWNING YOUR AUTHORITY

External authorities never control my feelings nor the conclusions I reach about them. No matter what takes place, I interpret it through my beliefs and have my particular emotional response accordingly. By increasing my awareness of my interpretations, having others with whom to check them out, getting honest feedback as well as having my feelings accepted and their expression encouraged, I am able to alter reaction patterns that may have been running my life. Regardless of what authority I may have given to others in my life before the Rebirth Training, this experience gives me the opportunity to reevaluate it and feel differently about it if I choose. For example, one of the women at the Training had been intimidated by a handsome, confident man around whom she felt afraid and concluded she was powerless. The heightened intensity of the atmosphere made these feelings all too apparent. She shared her feeling with me and then felt confident enough to share them with him. This in turn opened the door for her to reexamine how she had been viewing and treating herself (just as she had done in the presence of her father and brother) and to do something differently about which she felt much better. It is not just doctors or leaders who may be authority figures for me. I also give my authority to people I judge or look down upon. I let them dictate that I cannot feel OK, be open, have fun, etc. while they are around. I make them the authority for when I can feel good. The goals at the Training are for each participant to be able to feel good about themselves in the presence of anyone. Participants can take more responsibility for who they are, why they are here, why they invited those they did into their lives and how they can effect the changes that increase joy and creativity. This is the prevailing intention and all activities scheduled or spontaneous are useful to this end.

BEYOND LIMITS

The Rebirth Training weekend is an opportunity to lovingly explore options. Participants are encouraged to seek sharing and behaving in ways which go beyond their old negative limits. All limits that I have created had an original motive for safety combined with a belief in some outside dangers. For example, I may limit my contact with strangers because of a belief in their potential to hurt me. In the safety of the workshop setting I may risk initiating contact with someone I do not know for the purpose of feeling more at ease in this and other groups. I am giving myself the opportunity to expand my narrow limits and release the constricted feelings I ordinarily have in the presence of strangers. The caution I formerly had was not necessarily bad. It might have been useful as a third grader, given my family fears, walking through the city streets to school. However, I am no longer a third grader nor do I subscribe to all of my familial fears, nor do I wish to view the world as continually a dangerous place. I do need to create experiences which give me a greater sense of physical and emotional safety. Just hearing that I am OK is not enough. I must feel it and have this feeling reinforced. Any number of reactions may eventuate from my contact with a "stranger" in the Rebirth Training. A new friendship may develop or that person may not be ready for contact and withdraw. Regardless of the response I get, my commitment is to reduce my fear. The situation may present an opportunity to lessen my fear of their hurting me by either moving closer or farther away. I also have faith that who I chose was not by accident and that person has his own lesson to learn. This lesson may be how to open to more spontaneity or how to say no to contact when wanting to be alone. In either case, I increase my self–support and internal acceptance by taking care of myself regardless of the other's response. I reduce the need to make either of us not OK. Nor does this mean that I immediately put on a sunny face whatever response I get. The other's response to me may bring forth anger, sadness or fear. My lesson in this case is how to let that emotion lead me to more of what I really want. This may entail communicating my feelings or not or some combination thereof. But again, I am encouraged to try something new to increase my safety. If my habit has been to always blurt out my feelings on the spot, I may practice sitting with them for a while and being OK with that. On the other hand, if I have always kept my feelings hidden, I may share them as best I can.

In trying these experiments I may seemingly bring forth the very thing I feared most, e.g., I ask someone to go for a walk and they say no. It is precisely at this point that either I continue to support my intention of increasing self–acceptance, or I say internally "This proves I never should have risked opening up." I can go either way. I may on some level decide to go around experiencing rejection for a while before I move on to something else. This affords me the chance to witness all the "benefits" of acting rejected and to decide whether I still want to subscribe to them. "Being rejected" may justify my withdrawal to a safe distance and allow me to feel my anger. Gradually, perhaps with other's help, I may discover that there are ways to increase safety and feel anger without having to diagnose myself as rejectable material. These insights may be simple, pleasant discoveries or deep life–changing events. They may happen in the privacy of my room or in a group setting. They are what the Rebirth Training is all about. As my self–acceptance and safety grows through these experiences there are less and less "strangers" in my life.

Peggy's courage in healing with a "stranger" at the Rebirth Training was a turning point in her life leading her to change the quality of all of her relationships and eventually to being a rebirther and healing presence for others.

PEGGY, AGE 47
MASSAGE THERAPIST

I have had two very significant rebirths. The first one was my first experience at Transformation's Rebirth Training. I was rebirthing with a man that considered himself a healer and was very much into energies and balancing. I was going through a painful time in my life (contemplating divorce and involved in an intense extra–marital affair). As I began this particular rebirthing I was frightened, but also at my wits end and ready to go through anything to get myself out of the hopeless rut I had gotten myself into.

I began breathing on this hot and muggy afternoon with a willingness to open to whatever happened. Curt was very reassuring. After awhile I began to suffer great pains in my chest around my heart chakra. I felt like my chest was going to explode. I wanted to stop, but Curt kept quietly talking to me and encouraging me to continue and work through it. This is where I had first hand experience that if you are willing and continue to breathe it will bring you through the pain. I did continue to breathe as Curt put his hands on my chest and did some energy balancing. The pain continued and I had many visualizations of how I had put myself into such a degrading place and completely lost my center and any self–confidence that I had gotten through my many years of therapy. I made a decision to leave the man I was having an affair with even though it felt like my heart would break without him in my life. I felt a rebirth of a kind as I took control of my life once again. As this happened I began to cough and choke and spit up phlegm. The pain went away and I cried for a long time. Curt just held me and kept giving me affirmations about what I had done and would do. It was a turning point in my life.

The second very significant rebirthing session was with Jim the end of February of this year. I have been doing some very intense work on my transpersonal growth. Since that day at the Rebirth Training, I have relentlessly continued my search for my personal fulfillment. I have continued my work with Jim doing rebirthing and psychotherapy, I have attended many seminars and workshops on self–help and have been consistent at doing meditation on a regular basis along with much reading and retreating.

Two years ago I made a trip to California and spent several days by myself in prayer and meditation by the sea. I made a conscious decision to love myself and this was the beginning of a new understanding for me. I was committed to telling the truth and doing whatever it took for me to get clear about myself. I worked hard with relationships after my divorce and learned much. Then finally God dropped Grace on me and I felt like I had definitely turned a huge corner in my life. I wanted to surround myself with people who thought along the same lines as I did – I was no longer interested in material possessions and immediate gratification. I felt unconditional love for a man who was willing to share such a love of "the two having their own identity, living in the one." I was working on many issues of letting go of attachments, mostly emotional. I continued to deal strongly with my money issues. I began to see the "play" of life. I felt more love for myself and others – with no expectations! So on this particular day when I began to rebirth with Jim I was feeling very focused and centered. I began to breathe and it felt so good. There was a second of old stuff when I would drift off and check out – but all of a sudden some energy came over me and I started to breathe clearly and consistently. It felt like I could breathe forever; it was the most wonderful feeling.

Later that afternoon after our Rebirth Practicum was over Jim announced to the group as I was leaving to go home that he wanted to acknowledge what great rebirthing work I had done and that he wanted to affirm publicly that I had "made it" (through my birth drama). It was such wonderful affirmation of all the hard work I had been doing for so long. I had come a long way. Now I'm not fooling myself to believe that this is the end, but it certainly is nice to know I can take a small rest and give myself credit for work well done as I now move into a deeper level of growth. The gift I have gained to take with me on my journey is that of surrendering into the pain and fear and accepting and trusting that if you keep intention on Love everything will resolve for the common good. God bless everyone who has helped me along my way!

Since my fears and limits are not always the same as yours, what I go through at the Rebirth Training will be different than you. Each of us on a psychic level chooses what challenges we are to face. This may be quite dramatic for some and very peaceful for others. Both can be profound. Once the decision to engage in the Rebirth Training process is made, the process commences. Many folks are aware of going through a good portion of their training before they arrive on site. Fear and anticipation can be as useful beforehand as when there. Those close to Training participants, e.g., family, friends, also by extension engage in the process. One cannot change without opening the door for all. Often people who hear about the Rebirth Training project their biggest fears on it, sensing the power in the process. The truth is that when we experience a dramatic increase in freedom and love, we do not tend to engage in socially unacceptable or unusual behaviors. Our inner experience is one of joy and pleasure and we generally do not need to prove anything by breaking rules or attracting attention. The opposite is the case. That is, my heart opening gives me a greater feeling of community and safety with others, a sense of belonging naturally in the world and having a pride in ownership of it and care for it. Though we may engage in different challenges, when we release our fears the experience of oneness is quite similar.

Since the energy and intention of clearing is great at the Training, it may well bring out the hidden illusions of our minds so that we can dispel them. One woman who had a former, painful relationship with a drug addict walked into a room in which a man looked like he was "shooting up." This shocked and dismayed her terribly and she felt angry and betrayed because once again she was lured into an unsafe environment full of "hypocritical" spiritual people. She went through her feelings, eventually sharing them, seeing her investment in resurfacing these feelings which had not been fully released, forgiving herself and the others involved and reowning her safety. It was not until this entire process had been worked through that she found out that the supposed "junkie" she had discovered at the training was actually a diabetic who was self–administering insulin. By that time, it made little difference to her as she could handle her feelings and her relationship to him regardless of what he was doing because she had dealt with her own inner fears.

The lesson of reserving or releasing judgment is all–important in such an atmosphere. It is always myself that I am seeing and judging. It is my behavior that I am condemning. This is not to say that I should put on rose–colored glasses and pretend to let everything be OK. Sometimes communicating my judgments in a non–hostile way is the first step to unraveling them and often can be important input for the other also. It requires the faith that I would not be having such reactions unless it was calling for some sort of healing for me and also involving the other in some significant way. It is up to the other to discover what this way is, not for me to tell that person. Trying to change the other in order to make me feel better is a futile game. I can never control the other and my attempts to do so are part of my illusion that that world is not OK and that I will be fine when it changes. Releasing the other and taking care of me gives that person the invitation to do the same. The more I recognize and forgive myself for projection and judgment, the more instantaneous healing takes place. The Rebirth Training is a prime ground for this healing.

Not all of what appears to Training participants is difficult or challenging by any means. Indeed there are by far more joyous or miraculous happenings to integrate for most participants, for example: feeling my heart open to all, hearing a tree talk, encountering a guru in the woods, etc. The most challenging to us, I contend, is leaving our ordinary reality behind and accepting the call to live on higher and higher energy levels where our rules of reason and logic may not apply. I believe that the bridge to our next stage of evolution involves manifesting miracles. In the world of divine principles these apparent miracles are quite ordinary. But now they serve to jar us from our complacent illusions. At a Rebirth Training we create the space in our minds and hearts for the miraculous to manifest.

Each training has been unique in its themes, content, exercises, techniques, experiments and energy games, although a general format including the connected breathing technique and small group work has emerged as a constant. The rebirthing experience continues to provide a living model for the workings of the spirit of breath in community.

As Jim recounts, the effects of rebirthing within the context of a Rebirth Training community stay alive in his consciousness , reminding him of the "unity beyond time."

JIM, AGE 30
SOCIAL SERVICE
ADMINISTRATOR

I'm sitting in a large room at a retreat center in Green Lake, Wisconsin. The thirty–five or so people arranged in a circle have gathered for the biannual Rebirth Training. We are about to select partners for a rebirth exchange – a selection based upon intuition – something very threatening to this overly developed rational mind.

It took a whole year for that mind to overcome its initial repulsion to the glitzy, fad, pop, new age name of "rebirthing." (I still prefer "conscious breathing"). Eventually, thanks to the gentleness and patience of my friend Russell, I did overcome that initial reaction and had my first rebirth with Jim Morningstar, Ph.D., Certified Rebirther.

The sensation of being in a body with fingers, toes, arms and legs entirely disappeared into the intense ball of energy that was generated in that first session. Now, in a strange new place filled with people who are also mostly strange and new to me, I am to have my second rebirthing session.

As the group dissolves itself into pairs, I am drawn towards a woman who appears at least somewhat safe, motherly and non–threatening. Marda is smiling and chatting as the pairs leave the large meeting room for the relative privacy of the rooms down the hall.

I agree to breathe first, figuring I could just huff and puff, make a show of it and get this over with as quickly and painlessly as possible. I lie down on the mat and pull a blanket over my trembling body. Does she know how scared I am?

Marda seems to know what she's doing, sitting cross–legged above my head offering contact that's reassuring but not overwhelming. She has a way of making heavy matter light.

Eyes closed, I start to breathe. A little more rapidly and deeply than normal breathing, I make a conscious effort to connect the inhale to the exhale. Smooth and flowing like a sine wave – as if the in and out can no longer be separated – they begin to merge into one continuous breath.

The mind attempts to intercede with its usually incessant chatter: (Nothing's happening. I'm just lying here breathing. I'm OK. It's almost over now. I don't feel a thing. I must not be doing it right.) But, just as in the first session, I begin to feel a tingling in my fingers. It feels like (pins and needles) as if my hands fell asleep. I move them around, stretch them, shake them. No, it doesn't go away. It's starting to happen again, just like last time.

The tingling, vibrating sensation begins to spread into my hands and up my arms, across my chest and into my stomach. It builds in intensity, feeling almost as if an electric current is running through my body. I can't run away and I'm losing control. It's getting harder and harder to tell what's real and what isn't.

I reach out to touch something but keep my eyes closed, too afraid to open them. My right hand makes contact with something but I can't tell what it is – it feels as if my hand has melted into the object – as if the current flows from it right into my arm. Oh, yes, it's the bedspring tilted up against the wall, out of the way.

The energy continues to build, feeling almost like the shock from a wall outlet. I want contact. Marda is talking. She's saying something about (a lot of energy. It's shooting right off your head.) Her voice sounds strange – clear and yet distorted at the same time – as if it is coming down a long tube. I reach back over my head and feel the reassuring touch of another person.

As soon as we make contact I feel – not imagine, not visualize, not hallucinate, but actually feel – something touch the top of my head. It's slowly and firmly moving down from my crown towards my brow. It feels like someone is pushing an elastic band down over my head. Oh my God! I recognize this! I know this! I've been here before! I'm moving down the birth canal!

It moves over my head past my eyes, in an instant, even though they're still closed. Everything goes a soft, warm, inky black with tiny pin points of color – like stars in the night sky. I'm not sure what happens now. Somehow, I pass the "peak" and change places with Marda.

During her rebirthing, Marda immediately makes contact with some emotional material and breathes to resolve it.

More than a year later, sitting in the living room of my third floor walk–up, what does it mean? As my mind continues to loosen its death grip upon the world, my experience comes back from time to time. From the depths of darkness, individuality preserved, rising to light, unity realized beyond time, it comes back even in my third floor walk–up.

REBIRTHING AND YOUR CALL TO GREATNESS

Each of us has an inner call to greatness that is undeniable, persistent and life–saving. True greatness comes in the fulfillment of our heart's desire. Greatness is experienced in the embrace of our highest self, not in chasing the limited notions of our culture. Attempts to deny or repress our call leads to depression, sickness and death.

Following our call brings forth any and every challenge necessary for us to meet. Each of us is an epic novel in progress. Following our journey takes the most courage, perseverance and attention we can muster. Pitfalls include absorption in others' drama, belief in helplessness and resignation to anything less than greatness.

Greatness does not lie in the mind. We judge ourselves as up or down, good or bad, ahead or behind, day by day. Identification with our divine essence in the face of emotional and mental havoc allows our natural state of greatness to prevail over repetitious judgments. Boredom is the state of fixed, repetitious judgment. Ultimately, our judgments are not very interesting even though we can become temporarily fascinated or mesmerized by them. Only our greatness is of lasting interest.

Rebirthing is the most direct pathway I know to putting the mind in its place and reconnecting with the simplicity and power of our inner child.

Fairy tales and children's stories hint at the truth of our calling and have appeal to the young of heart. It is only "growing up" to a false idea of adulthood that leads to stagnation. Interest in fairy tales, however, is only inspirational. These stories pale in comparison to live challenges. Every hero's drama you have read is already part of you. The noble feelings they evoke are the baseline upon which you create your world anew. Each of us is the pioneer that must blaze the trails for all. Our phony adult self laughs at the story of the little boy or girl who saves the world by his or her single act of charity or bravery. This makes no sense to our rational belief system. In our hearts, however, we feel its truth and it touches us. Each of us is called to save the earth. Each is just as special and necessary as the other. We make this choice again and again, and it gets more easy and joyous as we do breath by breath.

When I truly open my heart through the spirit of breath, my life is the most interesting life to me that I ever heard of or read about. I believe that following your call to greatness makes your life the most exciting and challenging to you. Rebirthing is dedicated to the greatness in every person, that greatness that you experience in your heart through the spirit of breath, not the image of it in your mind. Mental and physical mastery calls you. You have what it takes to face your greatest challenges and come through victorious. I invite you to rediscover this and to use the powerful support and companionship of similarly motivated beings throughout the world and at Transformations, whether you simply connect with us in the spirit of breath or come to play and work with us in body.

APPENDIX I

REBIRTHING THROUGH PREGNANCY AND DELIVERY

ANNA, AGE 38
NURSE, REBIRTHER
DIRECTOR OF LIFE WAVES

An affirmation I use today in my ninth month of pregnancy is: My creative thought seeds soothe and stimulate natural wonder and gratitude for life in myself and the new being I still carry in my womb.

My first child, Mira's birth was very intimate, quiet and pleasing. She slipped out of my birth canal without a whimper and immediately opened her eyes to take in all of the faces and sights around her. Her name very appropriately means "to look" in Spanish. I was very thrilled and knew the efforts I made during that pregnancy to provide Mira with a safe and happy intrauterine life paid off. I became very determined to make my second and last birth even more pleasurable.

As soon as I knew of the second pregnancy I set out to enhance my physical and mental health in every possible way. The process involved: sleeping a lot, eating well, surrounding myself with quiet, uplifting music, being close to the lake and wooded areas in the nature preserve and parks nearby. I rebirthed once or twice monthly and got frequent massages. I took mineral and vitamin supplements and remedies to keep my body fluids in balance and strengthen my constitution.

Rebirthing I found became an especially powerful way for me to purify and ready myself for new life. During rebirths I was amazed at how attuned I felt to the little divine being inside and how this life in my womb drew me back to my own intrauterine experiences. Memories of being in my mother's womb, my birth and even my spiritual essence visualized in the form of a tiny cherub hovering about my parents before conception flowed through my awareness. I intuitively gained more understanding about the spiritual plane before birth as well as my eternal connectedness with others.

My rebirths during this pregnancy opened the way for more intimate and growthful family interactions. This included interactions with my own mother and father whose hearts warmed to the thought of a second grandchild. I began to relax my usual anxieties around my parents and felt them responding to my greater acceptance of them as they were. My maternal grandmother died during my eighth month of pregnancy. I marvel at how rebirthing with a trusted friend through her loss relieved me of painful feelings I didn't realize I still had about my family history, feelings that could easily touch and influence the new child.

I became especially fond of rebirthing in water, myself in luxurious baths and with my rebirther in the hot tub. Warm–water rebirthing reminded me fondly of my underwater experience snorkeling in the Caribbean during my early pregnancy with Mira. In this warm body of water teeming with life and growth, I remembered the embryonic feeling in the soft, womb–like body of water, just as my daughter at that point knew no boundaries in my womb. There we were, two tiny sea creatures swimming in our most primal, pleasurable environments. Underwater I felt awed and in total harmony with the little tad–pole like creature in my womb.

The rebirthing breath, connected, with a relaxed exhalation, became an easy breathing pattern for labor. Contractions became waves of energy with breath awareness, rather than pain. My daughter who was present at the birth seemed not at all frightened to be with her mom, who made some very loud and strange noises during the delivery, energizing to say the least. She became very excited, especially at the moment Andrea's head appeared, and began to sing "Jingle Bells." It felt like Christmas to her.

I'm pleased to recommend rebirthing for prospective mothers. I found it was a valuable tool in healing negative, suppressed emotions during pregnancy, labor and delivery. Though I had the usual discomforts, most of the feelings I had around birth were positive. My rebirths actually intensified the pleasures and beauty of the entire nine month experience.

The event of birth may seem very traumatic for the baby, LeBoyer points out. However, a well–prepared, gentle mother may help tremendously in easing this trauma for her child, influencing at that moment its entire life experience. Mothers who can instill some of their own joy and serenity into their newborn are truly blessings to their children.

APPENDIX II

THE SCHOOL OF SPIRITUAL PSYCHOLOGY

The SSP offers rebirthing by a staff of trained professionals. For those seeking training in becoming a rebirther, the SSP presents regular training experiences as well as a six–month Practicum in Rebirthing. Those completing the requirements for this practicum receive a certificate of completion in this training.

The SSP further offers a three year intensive program in personal growth and spiritual leadership leading to a Master of Spiritual Psychology Certificate.

Comprehensive Courses:

FIRST YEAR PROGRAM
November through May
The Personal Integration Program brings together essential elements of a whole person into an integrated, directed, successful individual. Program components include: Creative Life Series, Body Aliveness Series, Core PIP Group, weekend intensives and individual consultations.

SECOND YEAR PROGRAM

October through May. The Spiritual Leadership Program heightens the ability to hear and follow inner guidance and manifest personal value on the planet. Program individually designed by Faculty and participants, includes SLP Core Group and Support Group, weekend intensives, electives and individual consultations.

THIRD YEAR PROGRAM

September through May. The Graduate Apprenticeship Program perfects healing and esoteric arts and entrepreneurial skills – leading the practical life of a present day mystic. Apprenticeship with Director and selected teachers. Program leads to a Master of Spiritual Psychology Certificate.

Limited enrollment by application.

For information contact:

Jim Morningstar, Ph.D., Director
THE SCHOOL OF SPIRITUAL PSYCHOLOGY
4200 West Good Hope Road
Milwaukee, WI 53209–2250
414.351.5770...VOICE
414.351.5760...FAX

OM

NAMAH

SHIVAYA